Ready® | 2 Writing
INSTRUCTION

Curriculum Associates

Vice President of Product Development: Adam Berkin
Editorial Director: Katherine Rossetti
Editorial: Maura Piazza, Cindy Greene, Amy Weber, Sarah Glasscock, Cass O'Keefe, Teri Jones
Design/Production: William Gillis, Lisa Rawlinson, Polo Barrera, Ed Scanlon
Cover Designer: Matthew Pollock
Cover Illustrator: O'Lamar Gibson

ISBN 978-0-7609-9400-9
©2016—Curriculum Associates, LLC
North Billerica, MA 01862

30 29 28 27 26 25 24

802649

Acknowledgments

Passage Credits

AMAZING SHARKS! by Sarah L. Thomson. Text copyright © 2005 by Sarah L. Thomson. Reprinted by permission of Harper Collins.

WHEELS (SIMPLE MACHINES) by Patricia and David Armentrout. Text copyright © 2009 by Patricia and David Armentrout. Reprinted by permission of Rourke Publishing.

Illustration Credits

p. 45: Linda Bleck/Painted Words

p. 73: Polo Barrera

p. 101: Erwin Madrid

p. 105: Sam Valentino

pp. 132-133: Peter Bollinger

pp. 160-161: Colin Jack

pp. 162-163: Mark Collins/illustrationOnLine.com

Photography Credits

p. 14: Muskoka Stock Photos/Shutterstock (top)

p. 14: Tracy Whiteside/Shutterstock (left)

p. 14: Krasowit/Shutterstock (right)

pp. 14-15: Borja Andreu/Shutterstock (background)

p. 15: The Colonial Williamsburg Foundation (top)

p. 15: Ajakor/Shutterstock (left)

p. 15: Madlen/Shutterstock (right)

p. 16: C-BY-ND: Creative Commons By Attribution Non-Derivative (shelter)

p. 16: AnutkaT/Shutterstock (fuel)

p. 16: kirillov alexey/Shutterstock (trees)

p. 16: Lizzeth Montejano, aculturame.com (canoes)

p. 16: Dmitriy Raykin (plates)

p. 16: PRILL/Shutterstock (plates/background)

p. 17: C-BY-ND: Creative Commons By Attribution Non-Derivative (baskets)

p. 17: Le Do/Shutterstock (corn)

p. 17: Charles Butzin III/Shutterstock (dolls)

p. 17: Tony Campbell/Shutterstock (deer)

p. 17: HandmadePictures/Shutterstock (corn food)

p. 17: Marilyn Angel Wynn/Getty Images (clothing)

p. 17: Marilyn Angel Wynn/Getty Images (weapons)

p. 17: Marilyn Angel Wynn/Getty Images (deer food)

p. 42: New England Historic Genealogical Society

pp. 42-44: Lekovic Maja/Shutterstock (accent)

p. 43: New England Historic Genealogical Society

pp. 43, 44: Shpak Anton (background)

p. 44: Harris & Ewing/Library of Congress

p. 45: DeMih/Shutterstock (background)

p. 70: Mrs_ya/Shutterstock

p. 71: Dominika Sebjan/Getty Images

p. 72: Ragne Kabanova/Shutterstock

p. 73: ILeysen/Shutterstock (background)

p. 73: Tovovan/Shutterstock (browser)

p. 98: Willyam Bradberry/Shutterstock (background)

p. 98: Catmando/Shutterstock (top)

p. 99: Cory Smith/Shutterstock (bottom)

p. 99: Rich Carey/Shutterstock (background)

p. 100: daulon/Shutterstock (top)

p. 100: A Cotton Photo/Shutterstock (left)

p. 100: Willyam Bradberry/Shutterstock (background)

p. 128: Tomasz Trojanowski/Shutterstock

p. 128: Ziablik/Shutterstock (background)

p. 129: RonGreer.Com/Shutterstock (right)

pp. 129-131: L Turay/iStockphoto (background)

p. 130: sommthink/Shutterstock (floor)

p. 130: Max Topchii/Shutterstock (bottom)

pp. 130-131: nikkytok/Shutterstock (bottom)

p. 131: bergamont/Shutterstock (bottom)

p. 131: VERSUSstudio/Shutterstock (faucet)

p. 131: JIANG HONGYAN/Shutterstock (pizza cutter)

p. 131: H.Kan/Shutterstock (screwdriver)

p. 131: Hellen Sergeyeva/Shutterstock (doorknob)

pp. 132-133: Donald Sawvel/Shutterstock (blueprint)

pp. 132-133: STILLFX/Shutterstock (wood background)

p. 192: Maks Narodenko/Shutterstock (left)

p. 192: Alucard2100/Shutterstock (right)

p. 198: melis/Shutterstock

p. 204: arbit/Shutterstock

p. 206: Teguh Mujiono/Shutterstock (left)

p. 206: ayelet-keshet/Shutterstock (right)

p. 208: PinkPueblo/Shutterstock

p. 214: tropicdreams/Shutterstock (top)

p. 214: Graham Prentice/Shutterstock (bottom)

p. 228: VoodooDot/Shutterstock (left)

p. 228: John T Takai/Shutterstock (right)

p. 234: Pushkin/Shutterstock (right)

p. 234: MC Artworks/Shutterstock (left)

Table of Contents

Introduction

Writing

In each of the writing lessons, you will move through the following steps.

Step 1 Learn About Writing

Step 2 Unpack Your Assignment

Step 3 Read and Gather Evidence

Step 4 Plan

Step 5 Draft

Step 6 Revise

Step 7 Edit

Step 8 Publish and Share

Table of Contents continued

Language Handbook

Language Handbook *continued*

The Writing Path
Writing from Sources

Come with me on the Writing Path!

STEP 1
Learn About Writing

Find out what kind of writing you will do. Read a model of the writing type.
- **Opinion**
- **Informative**
- **Narrative**

STEP 5
Draft

📝 **Write Time** Begin your writing.

Write the:

BEGINNING

MIDDLE

END

STEP 6
Revise

📝 **Write Time** Revise your writing.

Make your writing the best it can be.

STEP 2
Unpack Your Assignment

📓 **Write Time** Read your assignment to discover what you will write about.

STEP 3
Read and Gather Evidence

📖 Read your texts and gather information to use in your writing.

Think It Through
Show what you know and get ready to write!

STEP 4
Plan

📓 **Write Time** Plan your writing.

Use the information you gathered from the texts to write about what you know.

STEP 7
Edit

📓 **Write Time** Edit your writing.

Check your spelling, grammar, and punctuation.

STEP 8
Publish and Share

📓 **Write Time** Share your writing with your friends!

You did it!
Let's celebrate!

W.2.2: Write informative/explanatory texts in which they introduce a topic, use facts and definitions to develop points, and provide a concluding statement or section.

Writing to Inform: Paragraph

Step 1 Learn About Informational Writing

What Is Information?

Information tells facts and details about a topic.

Here is some information about rabbits!

Rabbits are covered in fur. They eat grass and hay.

What Is Informational Writing?

Writers use facts to tell about real people, places, or things. Writers explain what something is, how something happened, or how something works.

Informational Writing has:

- a **beginning** that introduces the topic
- a **middle** that tells facts and details about the topic
- an **end** that sums up the information

Jayden wrote an informational paragraph telling what the Oglala Lakota people wear to a celebration. Let's read it.

MENTOR TEXT

Special Clothes for a Special Day

by Jayden Cook

Do you have special clothes for special days? Every August, the Oglala Lakota people in South Dakota have a celebration. They dress like their ancestors. Ancestors are the people who lived before them. Their ancestors wore dresses, pants, and moccasins made from animal skins. Moccasins are shoes. The Oglala also wore clothes with beautiful beads. Some of the beads showed animals. Some showed plants. The Oglala respect nature and their ancestors. They show this respect by wearing special clothing.

1 Did Jayden write a **beginning**? **Underline** his topic in green.

2 Did he write a **middle**? **Underline** facts and details about the topic in yellow.

3 Did he write the **end**? **Underline** sentences that sum up the information in red.

W.2.7: Participate in shared research and writing projects.

Step 2 Unpack Your Assignment

FOCUS Identify Assignment Details

Modeled Instruction

Let's see how Jayden unpacks his assignment.

Jayden's Assignment

? What special clothing do the Oglala Lakota wear for celebrations?

📖 Read an article about a special celebration called a powwow.

✏️ Write a paragraph for your teacher. Give information about the clothing the Oglala Lakota wear for special celebrations.

- In the **beginning** tell the topic.
- Give facts and details about the topic in the **middle**.
- Sum up the information at the **end**.

Think Aloud

? To answer this question, I need to know about the clothing the Oglala Lakota wear for a special celebration.

📖 I will look for details about clothing as I read the article.

✏️ I am writing a paragraph, and my teacher will read it. I need to include my topic, facts and details, and an ending that sums up the information.

Let's read and mark your assignment.

Write Time

Your Assignment

? How did the Powhatan people use natural resources?

📖 Read "My Dad Lives History" and "Nature's Resources."

✏️ Write a paragraph for your classmates. Tell about two resources the Powhatan people used.

- In the **beginning** tell the topic.
- Give facts and details about the topic in the **middle**.
- Sum up the information at the **end**.

1 Underline the question you will answer.

2 Draw a box around what you will write.

3 Circle who will read what you write.

Turn and Talk
What three parts will your paragraph have?

W.2.8: Recall information from experiences or gather information from provided sources to answer a question.

Step 3 Read and Gather Evidence

Source Text 1

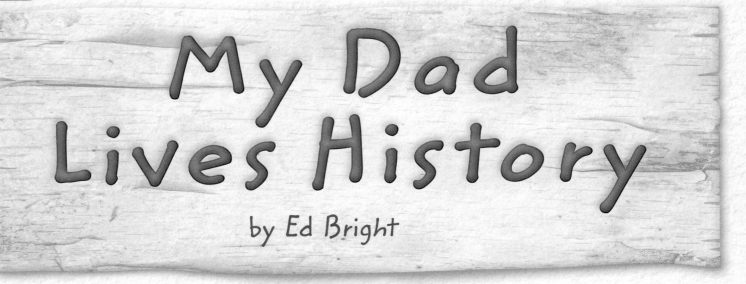

My Dad Lives History

by Ed Bright

1   My name is Ed. I am Powhatan. My dad has taught me a lot about our tribe. He works at a living history museum. He teaches visitors about Native Americans. Dad teaches visitors how Powhatan used resources. They used plants, water, and animals.

2   Where did the Powhatan find the resources they needed? They depended on their environment. Land and water were all around them. My dad helps visitors understand. He shows how the Powhatan used the land. They grew corn, beans, and squash. Powhatan used water from rivers to help grow the crops. They caught fish from the rivers.

Trout

My dad works with other actors to help people learn about the past.

Blueberries

Antlers

3   The Powhatan used the forest, too. They used trees to build homes. They rode in canoes made of trees. Oak trees also gave them acorns to eat. My dad shows visitors how to make flour out of acorns. The Powhatan used berries from the forest to make dye. Sometimes my dad shows how berries can color clothing and beads. The forests also had lots of deer. My dad explains that Powhatan ate deer meat. They used the skin to make clothing and shoes. They used the deer's antlers to make tools.

4   I am very proud of my dad. I am very proud to be Powhatan, too.

NATURE'S RESOURCES

The Powhatan people made good use of the plants and animals in their environment.

Shelter

Trees

Fuel

Canoes

Plates

Corn

Dolls

Food

Baskets

Clothing

Deer

Tools

Food

Think It Through

1 **Fill in** each chart. Use details from "My Dad Lives History" and "Nature's Resources."

Resource 1

Type
How did the Powhatan people use it?

HINT Think of how the Powhatan people used plants.

Resource 2

Type
How did the Powhatan people use it?

HINT Think of how the Powhatan people used animals.

Resource 3

Type
How did the Powhatan people use it?

HINT Reread "My Dad Lives History."

Resource 4

Type
How did the Powhatan people use it?

HINT Review the pictures in "Nature's Resources."

2 **Put a checkmark** beside the two resources you will write your paragraph about.

W.2.2: Write informative/explanatory texts in which they introduce a topic, use facts and definitions to develop points. . . .

Step 4 Plan

Modeled Instruction

Jayden gathered information from his sources. Then he planned the details to include in his paragraph.

Topic

The Oglala Lakota wear special clothes for a ceremony.

Detail

animal skin clothing and moccasins

Detail

1 **Fill in** the other detail that Jayden included in his paragraph.

Guided Practice

Use the organizer below to plan your writing.

2 **Write** your topic in the first box.

3 **Write** one detail in each box below your topic.

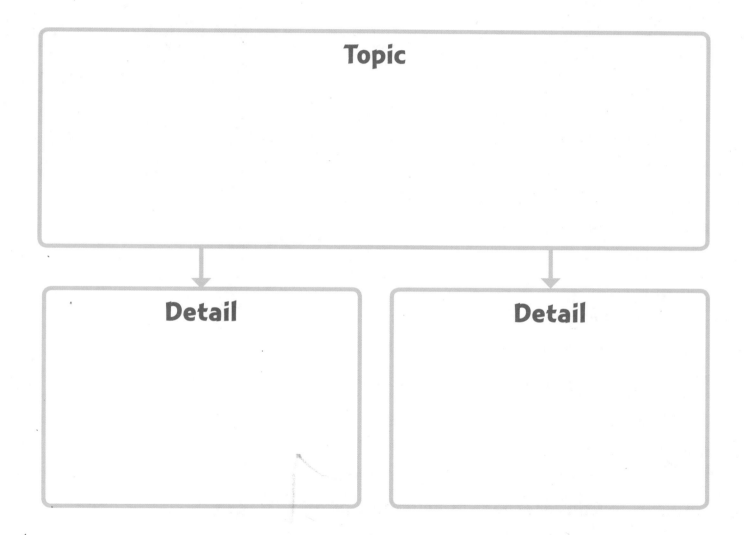

Topic

Detail

Detail

Independent Practice

Write Time Write a sentence about each of the resources you will include in your paragraph.

W.2.2: Write informative/explanatory texts in which they introduce a topic . . .

Step 5 Draft

This chart shows the parts of an informational paragraph. Use the ideas here as you draft your **beginning**, **middle**, and **end**.

Parts of an Informational Paragraph

BEGINNING	A strong **beginning** should:
Introduces the topic	• Tell the **topic** of the paragraph. • **Interest** readers.

MIDDLE	**Middle** sentences should:
Tells information about the topic	• Give **facts** that explain the topic. • Add **details** that give more information.

END	The **end** of your paragraph should:
Sums up the information	• **Connect** the facts with the topic in different words. • **Finish** your thoughts about the topic.

Write the BEGINNING

Study the beginning of Jayden's paragraph. Then try writing the beginning of your paragraph.

BEGINNING

MIDDLE

END

⭐ MENTOR TEXT

Do you have special clothes for special days? Every August, the Oglala Lakota people in South Dakota have a celebration. They dress like their ancestors. Ancestors are the people who lived before them.

1 **Draw a box** around the topic of Jayden's paragraph.

✏️ MY PARAGRAPH

2 **Write** two ways to introduce your topic.

- _____

_____

- _____

_____

HINT Make your readers want to learn more about your topic.

👤 Independent Practice

 Write Time Draft the beginning of your paragraph. Use the tips from the chart on page 22.

💬 Turn and Talk

Which of your partner's beginnings is better? Why?

W.2.2: . . . use facts and definitions to develop points, and provide a concluding statement or section.

Write the MIDDLE

Read one fact that Jayden added to the middle of his paragraph. Then try writing one of your facts.

BEGINNING

MIDDLE

END

MENTOR TEXT

The Oglala also wore clothes with beautiful beads. Some of the beads showed animals. Some showed plants.

1 **Underline** Jayden's fact about Oglala clothing.

2 **Draw a box** around the details that tell more about the fact.

MY PARAGRAPH

3 **Write** a sentence telling one of your facts. Add details to tell more about that fact.

HINT Review your chart on page 21.

_____

_____

_____

Write the END

Study the end of Jayden's paragraph. Then try writing the end of your paragraph.

BEGINNING

MIDDLE

END

⭐ **MENTOR TEXT**

The Oglala respect nature and their ancestors. They show this respect by wearing special clothing.

1 **Underline** the words that sum up Jayden's information.

✏️ **MY PARAGRAPH**

2 **Write** two different endings for your paragraph.

> **HINT** Connect your facts with the topic in different words.

* _____

  _____

* _____

  _____

Independent Practice

 Write Time Finish drafting the middle and end of your paragraph.

Turn and Talk 💬
How does your ending sum up your paragraph?

W.2.5: With guidance and support from adults and peers, focus on a topic and strengthen writing as needed by revising . . .

Step 6 Revise

FOCUS Organization and Focus

 Modeled Instruction

Let's read part of Jayden's draft and part of his checklist.

MENTOR TEXT Draft

> In August, the Oglala Lakota in South Dakota dress as their ancestors did for a special celebration. The Oglala hold many celebrations each year. Their ancestors wore dresses and pants made from animal skins. The moccasins on their feet came from animal skins too. They also wore clothing with beautiful beads. Some beads showed animals. Some showed plants.

Informational Writing Checklist

✔ Did I introduce the topic of my paragraph?

✔ Do my facts and details come from my sources?

✔ Do my facts and details tell more about my topic?

1 **Underline** Jayden's topic in green.

2 **Underline** his facts and details in yellow.

3 What detail does not tell about Jayden's topic?

_____

_____

Guided Practice

I wrote about how the Powhatan people used corn. Can you help me make my paragraph better?

The Powhatan people used resources in nature for everything they needed. Corn was very important. People still eat corn at picnics today. The Powhatan ate the corn. They also made dolls and baskets from the husks.

1 **Underline** Hershel's topic in green.

2 **Underline** his facts and details in yellow.

3 What detail does not tell about how the Powhatan people used corn as a resource?

_____

_____

HINT Everything in Hershel's paragraph should be about the topic.

Independent Practice

 Write Time Use the Informational Writing Checklist to help you revise your writing.

Turn and Talk
Why is it important for every detail to tell more about the topic?

FOCUS Facts and Opinions

Modeled Instruction

A **fact** is information that is true. An **opinion** is the way a person thinks or feels about something.

When you write an informational paragraph,

- check your facts in a trusted source to make sure they are true.

- do not include sentences that show your opinion.

Let's see how Jayden revised his paragraph for facts and opinions.

MENTOR TEXT Draft

In the spring, the Oglala Lakota people in South Dakota dress as their ancestors did for a special celebration. I think it would be a lot of fun to go. Their ancestors wore dresses, pants, and moccasins made from animal skins.

Think Aloud

- I'll check my source to make sure the celebration happens in spring. Oh, it happens in August. I will revise this sentence.

- This sentence is not a fact. The words "I think" mean that it is my opinion. I'll take it out.

Guided Practice

Read each sentence pair. **Underline** the sentence that belongs in an informational paragraph.

1 It would be great to make clothes like the Oglala did.

The Oglala wore clothes with beautiful beads.

HINT An opinion is the way a person feels about something.

2 Deer skins were made into pants and moccasins.

Deer skins probably made really comfortable clothing.

3 The Powhatan people show respect for nature by not being wasteful.

I can't believe how many resources the Powhatan people used!

HINT A fact is something you can check in a source.

Independent Practice

Write Time Check the facts in your paragraph. Take out any opinion words or sentences.

Turn and Talk
Why should you leave your opinions out of informational writing?

Step 7 Edit

W.2.5: With guidance and support from adults and peers, focus on a topic and strengthen writing as needed by . . . editing.

L.2.2a: Capitalize holidays, product names, and geographic names.

FOCUS Capitalization

Modeled Instruction

When you **capitalize** a word, you write the first letter in uppercase. The other letters are lowercase.

Remember to capitalize:

- countries, mountains, states, and parks

- holidays, months, and days

- people or groups of people

- words that begin a sentence

Read part of Jayden's draft below.

Language Handbook To learn more about capitalization, turn to page 208.

MENTOR TEXT Draft

Every August, the Oglala Lakota people in south dakota have a celebration. They dress like their ancestors.

1 **Circle** the capitalized word that names a month.

2 **Underline** the phrase that names a group of people.

3 **Capitalize** the words that name a state.

Guided Practice

Rewrite each sentence. Capitalize words correctly.

4 the powhatan people lived in virginia.

_____

HINT Reread the list on page 30.

5 how do you use resources?

_____

6 people in south dakota celebrate native americans' day.

_____

HINT Which words or phrases are proper nouns?

7 how did ed learn about the powhatan people?

_____

Independent Practice

Write Time Check that you capitalized words in your paragraph correctly. Check your spelling and punctuation, also.

Turn and Talk
When should you capitalize a word?

W.2.6: With guidance and support from adults . . .
produce and publish writing, including in collaboration
with peers.

Step 8 Publish and Share

FOCUS Illustrate Facts

 Prepare

Now it's time to share! You can show what you have learned by
illustrating facts from your writing.

Read the fact below. Then **draw** a picture to illustrate the fact.

> FACT   *The Powhatan people used trees to build canoes.*

Write an interesting fact from your paragraph. Then **draw** a picture to illustrate the fact.

FACT

Independent Practice

 Write Your Informational Paragraph

How did the Powhatan people use natural resources?

W.2.3: Write narratives in which they recount a well elaborated event or short sequence of events, include details to describe actions, thoughts, and feelings, use temporal words to signal event order, and provide a sense of closure.

Writing a Narrative: Paragraph

Step 1 Learn About Narrative Writing

What Is a Narrative?

A narrative tells a made-up or a real story. The characters can be people or plants, animals, and objects that behave like people.

I wrote a story about a dragon's trip to the moon.

I also wrote a story about my vacation.

What Is Narrative Writing?

Writers tell a story about one or more events. They include details to describe how characters think, feel, and act.

Narrative Writing has:

• a **beginning** that introduces the characters and setting

• a **middle** that shows how the characters think, feel, and act

• an **end** that finishes the story and makes sense

Ava wrote a narrative paragraph that retells some important events in George Washington Carver's life. Let's read it.

MENTOR TEXT

The Plant Doctor
by Ava Johnson

George Washington Carver was born in Missouri around 1864. George first became interested in plants as a little boy. He decided to create a special garden. He watched the plants and learned. "Show me how you grow," he whispered. Then one day, a woman asked George to look at a rosebush. "It won't bloom!" she said. George moved the woman's rosebush into the sun. Soon, beautiful roses covered the bush. People began calling George the "Plant Doctor." Later, when George grew up, he helped solve farmers' problems all over the country.

1 Did Ava write a **beginning**? **Underline** the characters and setting in green.

2 Did she write a **middle**? **Underline** details about how the characters think, feel, or act in yellow.

3 Did she write the **end**? **Underline** the words that finish the story in red.

Step 2 Unpack Your Assignment

 Modeled Instruction

Let's see how Ava unpacks her assignment.

⭐ Ava's Assignment

? How did George Washington Carver become the "Plant Doctor"?

📖 Read two stories about George Washington Carver.

✏️ Write a narrative paragraph for your family. Tell the story of how George Washington Carver became the "Plant Doctor."

- In the **beginning** introduce the characters and setting.
- In the **middle** describe how the characters think, feel, and act.
- Tell what happens at the **end**.

Think Aloud

? To answer this question, I need to learn about a man named George Washington Carver.

📖 I will look for details about how he became the "Plant Doctor" when I read these stories.

✏️ I am writing a narrative paragraph, and my family will read it. I will tell who is in the story, what happens, and where it happens.

Let's read and mark your assignment.

Write Time

Your Assignment

? How did Helen Keller learn that letters form words?

📖 Read "Seeing Differently" and "Helen Keller: A Picture Story."

✏️ Write a narrative paragraph for your family. Tell the story of how Helen Keller learned her first word in sign language.

- In the **beginning** introduce the characters and setting.

- In the **middle** describe how the characters think, feel, and act.

- Tell what happens at the **end**.

1 **Underline** the topic of your story.

2 **Draw a box** around what you will write.

3 **Circle** who will read what you write.

Turn and Talk
What should each part of your paragraph include?

W.2.8: Recall information from experiences or gather information from provided sources to answer a question.

Step 3 Read and Gather Evidence

Source Text 1

❖ Seeing Differently ❖

by Amy Lin

1 Helen Keller was born in Alabama in 1880. She got very sick as a baby. Her sickness left her blind and deaf. She could not see or hear. A teacher named Anne Sullivan came to work with Helen. She tried to teach Helen words. She made signs for letters on Helen's hand. For many weeks, Miss Sullivan was unsuccessful. Then one day, she had an idea.

Anne Sullivan

2   Helen understood the letter signs that I made on her hand, but she did not know that the letters formed words. I tried many different words. Then one day we walked near the water pump. I put Helen's hand under the cool stream, and I made the letter signs for W-A-T-E-R in her other hand. I repeated this many times. Helen's face lit up. She danced with joy. Finally, Helen knew the letters I wrote in her hand meant *water*.

Helen Keller

3   I remember when Miss Sullivan made the letters W–A–T–E–R in my hand. I did not know those letters spelled a word. Then I felt something cool and wet. Miss Sullivan made the letters again, more quickly. My hand felt wet again, and I tasted it. It was water! I finally understood. Miss Sullivan spelled the word *water*. Water is what I felt on my hand! We returned to the house, where Miss Sullivan taught me many more words.

Helen as a grown woman.

4   With a lot of hard work, Helen Keller learned to write and speak. She traveled around the world and helped others who were blind and deaf. Helen often retold her story of the water pump. She was always grateful to her teacher, Miss Sullivan.

Helen Keller:
A Picture Story
Illustrated by Linda Bleck

First

But

Then

Finally

Think It Through

1 **Fill in** the charts using details from "Seeing Differently" and "Helen Keller: A Picture Story."

Characters

Name one character.	
Describe this character.	

> **HINT** What are her traits? What else do you know about her?

Name another character.	
Describe this character.	

> **HINT** What would you tell someone who has never heard of her?

Setting

Where did this story happen?

When did this story happen?

HINT Where were they standing? What time of day was it?

Events

Describe a problem the characters faced.

Tell how the problem was solved.

HINT Reread page 43. What did Anne do?

W.2.3: . . . recount a . . . short sequence of events . . .

Step 4 Plan

FOCUS Organize Your Details

Modeled Instruction

Ava made a plan before she wrote. She thought about how George became the "Plant Doctor."

The Plant Doctor

First	George became very interested in plants. He created a special garden.

↓

Then	A woman asked George to help with a rosebush.

↓

Last	Roses covered the bush. George was called the "Plant Doctor."

1 **Write** another detail in the middle.

Use the sequence chart to plan your writing.

2 **Write** the events for your narrative in order.

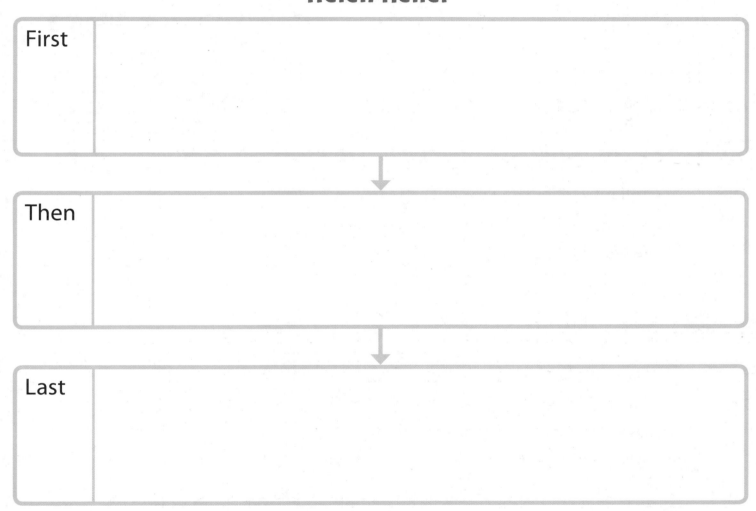

Helen Keller

First	
Then	
Last	

Independent Practice

Write Time Write a sentence telling how Anne and Helen felt at the end of the story.

W.2.3: Write narratives in which they recount a . . .
short sequence of events . . .

Step 5 Draft

This chart shows the parts of a narrative paragraph. Use the ideas here as you draft your **beginning**, **middle**, and **end**.

Parts of a Narrative Paragraph

BEGINNING	A strong **beginning** should:
Introduces characters and setting	• Tell **who** is in the story. • Tell **where** and **when** the story takes place.
MIDDLE	**Middle** sentences should:
Describes the events	• Use details to describe how the characters **think, feel,** and **act.** • Use **time-order words** to tell the events in order.
END	The **end** of your story should:
Tells how the story ends	• Make **sense.** • Make the story feel **finished.**

Write the BEGINNING

Study the beginning of Ava's paragraph. Then try writing the beginning of your paragraph.

BEGINNING

MIDDLE

END

⭐ MENTOR TEXT

> George Washington Carver was born in Missouri around 1864. George first became interested in plants as a little boy.

1️⃣ **Draw a box** around the character in Ava's story.

2️⃣ **Underline** the setting of the story.

✏️ MY PARAGRAPH

3️⃣ **Write** two different beginnings for your paragraph.

HINT Introduce your characters and setting.

- _____

  _____

- _____

  _____

👤 Independent Practice

 Write Time Draft the beginning of your paragraph. Use the tips from the chart on page 50.

Turn and Talk 💬

Compare your two beginnings. Which is better? Why?

W.2.3: Write narratives in which they recount a well elaborated event or short sequence of events, include details to describe actions, thoughts, and feelings . . . and provide a sense of closure.

Write the MIDDLE

Read one event that Ava added to the middle of her paragraph. Then try writing one of your events.

BEGINNING
MIDDLE
END

> George first became interested in plants as a little boy. He decided to create a special garden. He watched the plants and learned. "Show me how you grow," he whispered.

1 **Circle** a detail that shows how George feels about plants.

2 **Underline** details that show what George does.

MY PARAGRAPH

3 **Write** a sentence describing one event in Helen's story. Add details showing what the characters think, feel, or do.

HINT Use your sequence chart on page 49 to remember your details.

_____

_____

_____

Write the END

Study the end of Ava's paragraph. Then try writing the end of your paragraph.

BEGINNING
↓
MIDDLE
↓
END

⭐ **MENTOR TEXT**

> People began calling George the "Plant Doctor." Later, when George grew up, he helped solve farmers' problems all over the country.

1 **Underline** the words that help Ava finish the story.

✏️ **MY PARAGRAPH**

2 **Write** two different endings for your paragraph.

- _____

  _____

- _____

  _____

HINT What happened after Helen learned her first word?

👤 **Independent Practice**

 Write Time Finish drafting the middle and end of your paragraph.

💬 **Turn and Talk**
How does your ending make your story feel finished?

W.2.5: With guidance and support from adults and peers, focus on a topic and strengthen writing as needed by revising . . .

Step 6 Revise

FOCUS Organization

Modeled Instruction

Let's read part of Ava's draft and part of her checklist.

MENTOR TEXT Draft

George Washington Carver was born in Missouri around 1864. George first became interested in plants as a little boy. He created a special garden. A woman asked George to look at a rosebush. It wouldn't bloom. Then the rosebush started to bloom. George moved it into the sun.

Narrative Writing Checklist

✔ Did I introduce the characters?

✔ Did I introduce the setting?

✔ Did I tell the events in order?

1 **Underline** Ava's character and setting in green.

2 **Underline** details that show what happened in yellow.

3 How can Ava improve her paragraph?

_____

_____

Guided Practice

I wrote about an important moment in Helen Keller's life. Can you help me make my paragraph better?

Helen Keller couldn't see or hear. Anne Sullivan was trying to teach Helen how to understand words. Anne made the letter signs for W-A-T-E-R in Helen's hand. Helen and Anne went to the water pump. Then Helen understood.

4 **Underline** the characters in green.

5 **Underline** details about what happened in yellow.

6 How can Hershel improve his paragraph?

_____

_____

HINT Look for sentences with actions.

Independent Practice

 Write Time Use the Narrative Writing Checklist to help you revise your writing.

Turn and Talk
How else could Hershel revise his writing?

Modeled Instruction

You can improve your narrative by adding **time-order** words. These words tell the order of events.

Time-Order Words		
first	next	then
later	soon	finally

Let's see how Ava used time-order words in her paragraph.

MENTOR TEXT

George first became interested in plants as a little boy. He decided to create a special garden. He watched the plants and learned. "Show me how you grow," he whispered. Then one day, a woman asked George to look at a rosebush.

Think Aloud

- The word *first* shows the beginning of how George became the "plant doctor."

- The word *then* tells my readers that another event is happening, after the first event.

Guided Practice

Revise each sentence pair. **Circle** the time-order word that makes the order of events clear.

1 George dug up a tiny plant. He carried it carefully to his garden.

George dug up a tiny plant. (First, Then) he carried it carefully to his garden.

HINT Which word tells what happened after George dug up the plant?

2 He looked for a long time. He studied the rosebush.

(First, Finally) he looked for a long time. He studied the rosebush.

HINT Which word tells how George began to solve the problem?

3 George studied peanut plants for many years. He understood how the plants could help farmers.

George studied peanut plants for many years. (Next, Finally) he understood how the plants could help farmers.

HINT Which word means "after a long time"?

Independent Practice

 Write Time Try adding time-order words to your paragraph.

Turn and Talk
How do time-order words improve your writing?

Step 7 Edit

W.2.5: With guidance and support from adults and peers, focus on a topic and strengthen writing as needed by . . . editing.

L.2.2c: Use an apostrophe to form . . . frequently occurring possessives.

FOCUS Possessive Nouns

Modeled Instruction

A **possessive noun** shows that a person or group of people owns something. Here is how you form possessive nouns.

Language Handbook To learn more about possessive nouns, turn to page 214.

Forming Possessive Nouns	
Singular	Add apostrophe (') and –s: Helen's hand
Plural	Add apostrophe (') after –s: students' books

Read part of Ava's draft below.

MENTOR TEXT Draft

George moved the woman's rosebush into the sun. Soon, beautiful roses covered the bush. When George grew up, he helped solve the problems of many farmers all over the country.

1 **Circle** the possessive noun.

2 **Underline** words that could be revised with a possessive noun.

3 **Write** the revised possessive noun.

_____

Revise each sentence. Form a possessive noun.

4 Anne used the doll that belonged to Helen.

HINT Whose doll is it?

_____

5 Helen did not know the meaning of the letters.

_____

6 Helen touched the face of the doll.

HINT The phrase *of the* means "belonging to."

_____

7 Helen did not understand the lessons from Anne.

_____

Independent Practice

Write Time Check that you used possessive nouns correctly. Check your spelling, capitalization, and punctuation, also.

Turn and Talk How can you remember where to put the apostrophe in a possessive noun?

Step 8 Publish and Share

W.2.6: With guidance and support from adults . . .
produce and publish writing, including in collaboration
with peers.

FOCUS Shared Retelling

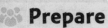 **Prepare**

Listen carefully as your classmate tells part of Helen's story. **Draw** what your classmate describes. Then **write** one or more sentences to label each picture.

BEGINNING

> **HINT** Introduce your characters.

Helen Keller became blind and deaf when she was young. Anne Sullivan came to teach her.

Share

MIDDLE

HINT What did Anne struggle to teach Helen?

END

HINT What happened at the water pump?

Independent Practice

 Write Your Narrative Paragraph

How did Helen Keller learn that letters form words?

W.2.1: Write opinion pieces in which they introduce the topic or book they are writing about, state an opinion, supply reasons that support the opinion, use linking words (e.g., *because, and, also*) to connect opinion and reasons, and provide a concluding statement or section.

Writing an Opinion: Paragraph

Step 1 Learn About Opinion Writing

What Is an Opinion?

Opinions tell what we like or what we would choose.

I love to swim! Do you? What's your opinion?

My favorite food is grass. What's your opinion?

What Is Opinion Writing?

Writers tell their feelings about a topic. Writers also give reasons to support their opinions. Readers want to know why the writer has that opinion.

Opinion Writing has:

- a **beginning** that introduces the topic and opinion

- a **middle** that gives reasons

- an **end** that makes the opinion clear

Luke wrote an opinion paragraph about a house that would be hard to build where he lives. Let's read it.

MENTOR TEXT

Too Warm for an Igloo
by Luke Weber

Would it be harder to build log houses or igloos where I live? I think building igloos would be much harder. It would be harder because we don't get snow and ice here. I live in Florida. We might get a little bit of snow sometimes. But it's not enough snow to build igloos. Also, igloos would melt if we built them. It's very warm in Florida. It can be really hot! Igloos would melt very quickly. The weather where I live makes building an igloo impossible.

1 Did Luke write a **beginning**? **Underline** his topic and opinion in green.

2 Did he write a **middle**? **Underline** his reasons in yellow.

3 Did he write the **end**? **Underline** the words that tell his opinion again in red.

W.2.7: Participate in shared research and writing projects.

Step 2 Unpack Your Assignment

Modeled Instruction

Let's see how Luke unpacks his assignment.

Luke's Assignment

? Would it be harder to build a log cabin or an igloo where you live?

📖 Read a chapter about igloos and an article about log cabins.

✏ Write a paragraph for your teacher. Share your opinion about which house would be harder to build where you live.

- In the **beginning** tell the topic and your opinion.
- Give two reasons in the **middle** that tell why.
- Tell your opinion in different words at the **end**.

Think Aloud

? To answer this question, I need to know how to build a log cabin and an igloo.

📖 I will look for those details when I read these sources.

✏ I am writing a paragraph, and my teacher will read it. I will make sure it has my topic, my opinion, two reasons, and my opinion in different words.

Let's read and mark your assignment.

Write Time

Your Assignment

? Which home would be the most fun for a weekend visit?

📖 Read "Unusual Homes" and "What's Inside?"

✏️ Write a paragraph for your friends. Share your opinion about which home would be the most fun.
- In the **beginning** tell the topic and your opinion.
- Give two reasons in the **middle** that tell why.
- Tell your opinion in different words at the **end**.

1 **Underline** the question you will answer.

2 **Draw a box** around what you will write.

3 **Circle** who will read what you write.

Turn and Talk
What should each part of your paragraph include?

W.2.8: Recall information from experiences or gather information from provided sources to answer a question.

Step 3 Read and Gather Evidence

Source Text 1

Unusual Homes

by Luis Vargas

1   Homes come in all shapes and sizes. Have you ever heard of a home on the water? You may have seen a tree house or played in one. Can you imagine living in a different kind of home?

A Home in the Trees

2   Tree houses are made of things from the environment, or the land, water, and air around us. Those things are called resources. People use the resources to build tree houses. They use wood from trees and they use the tree itself! They may collect rainwater to use for a shower. They may even use sunlight for heat!

3   Some tree houses are simple. Others are very fancy with bedrooms, a kitchen, a bathroom, and a living room, too!

The tree house doesn't hurt the tree.

This house is made with thousands of bottles.

A House of Bottles

4   It takes a lot of energy to recycle bottles. Some people have found a way to reuse them. This house is made of bottles! People reuse all kinds of bottles. They use plastic bottles. They use glass bottles. They put the bottles next to each other like bricks. They don't have to use cement to make them stick together. Sand and dried mud work, too. The bottles are side by side. They make a wall or a roof. They keep the cold winter air outside and warm air inside. People help the environment when they reuse bottles. They don't need to use wood from trees.

A Home that Floats

5   Have you heard of a houseboat? It's one way to live while taking a ride on the water. Many houseboats look mostly like boats. Some houseboats stay in one place. They are tied to a dock. Other houseboats travel from place to place using powerful motors. You can sit out on the porch to go fishing. You can tuck yourself into bed as the houseboat floats. You can sail on the water while you sleep!

6   Wouldn't it be fun to stay in one of these special houses? Let's go!

This houseboat is on the move.

http://www.bikehomes.pin/whatsinside

What's Inside?

Peek inside this tiny house on the back of a bicycle.

There's a **light** for reading at night.

The **windows** let in air and light.

The **bed** is up high.

There is a **kitchen** to prepare food.

The **generator** makes power for the light and television.

There is **storage** to keep the home neat.

The **bicycle** helps move the home from place to place.

Think It Through

1 Fill in each chart. Use details from "Unusual Homes" and "What's Inside?"

Tree House

Reason Why It Would Be Fun
Detail from the Text

HINT Use the same words as the text.

Bottle House

Reason Why It Would Be Fun
Detail from the Text

HINT What makes this house special?

Houseboat

Reason Why It Would Be Fun

house boat i

Detail ~~from the Text~~ whcn
swim
yoo cen ewan

HINT Picture yourself inside this kind of house.

Bicycle House

Reason Why It Would Be Fun

Detail from the Text

HINT What do you notice in the picture?

2 **Put a checkmark** beside the home you will write your paragraph about.

W.2.1: . . . state an opinion, supply reasons that support the opinion . . .

Step 4 Plan

Modeled Instruction

Luke made a plan before he wrote. He thought about why building an igloo might be hard.

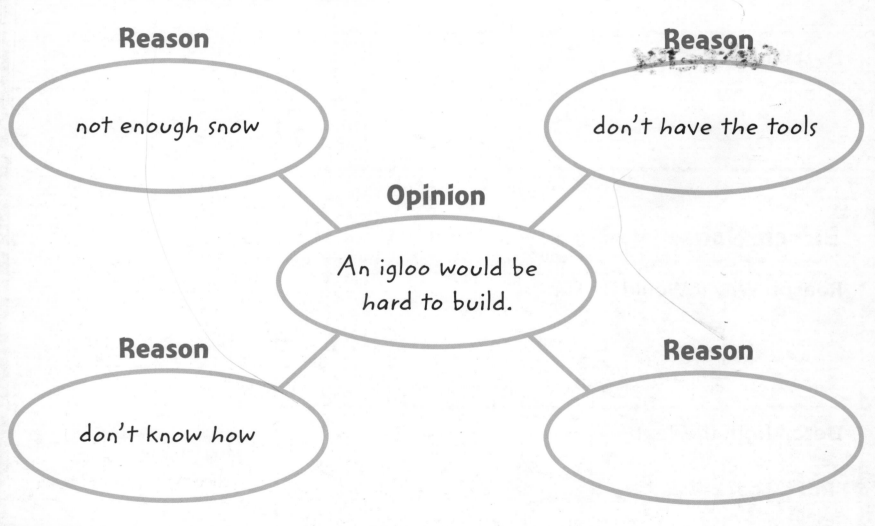

Reason

not enough snow

Reason

don't have the tools

Opinion

An igloo would be hard to build.

Reason

don't know how

Reason

1 **Fill in** the blank space with the other reason Luke included in his paragraph.

2 **Put a checkmark** beside each reason Luke used when he wrote his paragraph.

Use the web below to plan your writing.

3 **Write** the home you would like to visit in the center.

4 **Write** your reasons in the outer spaces.

Reason

you
couu.
swim

Reason

I covid dec
thejuma off

Opinion

hous edaat

Reason

you
3ould a
water
Siiho Have

Reason

you
covld
fish

5 **Put a checkmark** beside the two reasons you will
include in your paragraph.

Independent Practice

Write Time Write a sentence that tells each reason
you chose.

W.2.1: Write opinion pieces in which they introduce the topic or book, state an opinion. . . .

Step 5 Draft

This chart shows the parts of an opinion paragraph. Use the ideas here as you draft your **beginning**, **middle**, and **end**.

Parts of an Opinion Paragraph

BEGINNING	
States your opinion about the topic	A strong **beginning** should: • Tell what the paragraph **is about.** • State your **opinion** about the topic. • **Interest** readers.

MIDDLE	
Gives reasons to support your opinion	**Middle** sentences should: • Give **reasons** for your opinion. • Give **support** for each of your reasons.

END	
Sums up how you feel about the topic	The **end** of your paragraph should: • **Tie together** your opinion and the topic. • Tell your opinion in **different words.**

Write the BEGINNING

Study the beginning of Luke's paragraph. Then try writing the beginning of your paragraph.

BEGINNING

MIDDLE

END

⭐ MENTOR TEXT

> Would it be harder to build log houses or igloos where I live? I think building igloos would be much harder.

1 **Circle** the topic of Luke's paragraph.

2 **Underline** the sentence that tells Luke's opinion.

✏️ MY PARAGRAPH

3 **Write** two different beginnings for your paragraph.

- _____

  _____

  _____

HINT You may begin with a question or a statement.

- _____

  _____

👤 Independent Practice

📓✏️ **Write Time** Draft the beginning of your paragraph. Use the tips from the chart on page 78.

Turn and Talk 💬
What makes your beginning interesting to readers?

W.2.1: Write opinion pieces in which they . . . supply reasons that support the opinion . . . and provide a concluding statement or section.

Write the MIDDLE

Read one reason that Luke added to the middle of his paragraph. Then try writing one of your reasons.

BEGINNING

MIDDLE

END

⭐ **MENTOR TEXT**

It would be harder because we don't get snow and ice here. I live in Florida. We might get a little bit of snow sometimes. But it's not enough snow to build igloos.

1 **Underline** the reason Luke gives.

2 **Draw a box** around the sentences that tell more about his reason.

✏️ **MY PARAGRAPH**

3 **Write** one of your reasons. Add a sentence to tell more about the reason.

HINT Use your word web on page 77 to remember your reasons.

_____

_____

_____

Write the END

Study the end of Luke's paragraph. Then try writing the end of your paragraph.

BEGINNING

MIDDLE

END

⭐ **MENTOR TEXT**

> Igloos would melt very quickly. The weather where I live makes building an igloo impossible.

1 **Underline** the words that tell Luke's opinion again.

✏️ **MY PARAGRAPH**

2 **Write** two different endings for your paragraph.

HINT Remind the reader of your topic.

* _____

_____

* _____

_____

👤 **Independent Practice**

 Write Time Continue drafting the middle and end of your paragraph.

💬 **Turn and Talk**
How do the middle and end of your paragraph connect to the beginning?

Step 6 Revise

W.2.5: With guidance and support from adults and peers, focus on a topic and strengthen writing as needed by revising . . .

FOCUS Organization

 Modeled Instruction

Let's read Luke's draft and part of his checklist.

MENTOR TEXT Draft

> Would it be harder to build log houses or igloos where I live? I think building igloos would be much harder. It would be harder because we don't get snow and ice here. I live in Florida. We might get a little bit of snow sometimes. But it's not enough snow to build igloos. I think building igloos would be much harder.

Opinion Writing Checklist

✔ Did I state my opinion?

✔ Did I give reasons for my opinion?

✔ Did I use different words to tell my opinion again?

1 Underline Luke's opinion in green.

2 Underline his reasons in yellow.

3 Give Luke two ways to improve his paragraph.

It kood be a good thing case

I wrote about the unusual home I would like to visit. Can you help me make my paragraph better?

Where would I like to spend a weekend? I think a houseboat would be a great place to visit. It would be fun because I love being on the water. I also think it would be fun because the houseboat could go different places.

4 **Underline** Hershel's opinion in green.

5 **Underline** his reasons in yellow.

6 What did Hershel forget to do at the end?

a good ne s i u

Independent Practice

 **Write Time** Use the Opinion Writing Checklist to help you revise your writing.

Turn and Talk
Give Hershel two ideas for a new ending.

Lesson 3 **Step 6 Revise** continued

W.2.1: . . . use linking words (e.g., *because, and, also*) to connect opinion and reasons . . .

FOCUS Linking Words

Modeled Instruction

One way to improve your opinion paragraph is to use **linking words.** They connect reasons to your opinion.

Linking Words		
Add a Detail	also	another
Show Cause and Effect	because	so

Let's see how Luke used linking words in his paragraph.

MENTOR TEXT

I think building igloos would be much harder. It would be harder because we don't get snow and ice here. I live in Florida. We might get a little bit of snow sometimes. But it's not enough snow to build igloos. Also, igloos would melt if we built them.

Think Aloud

- The word *because* links my opinion to my first reason. I think it would be too hard to build an igloo. My reason is that we don't get enough snow or ice.

- The word *also* connects my opinion to my second reason. *Also* means "another" or "in addition to."

Guided Practice

Revise each sentence pair. **Circle** the linking word that connects the two ideas.

1 We don't build igloos here because there is no snow. An igloo would melt in the hot weather.

We don't build igloos here because there is no snow. (Also, Because) an igloo would melt in the hot weather.

HINT Which linking word adds a second reason?

2 It would be hard to build an igloo. It is too hot here in Florida.

It would be hard to build an igloo (another, because) it is too hot here in Florida.

HINT Which linking word tells why?

3 We don't get much snow in Florida. We can't build an igloo.

We don't get much snow in Florida, (because, so) we can't build an igloo.

Independent Practice

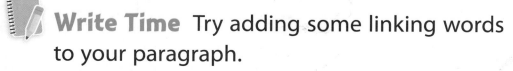 **Write Time** Try adding some linking words to your paragraph.

Turn and Talk
How do linking words improve your writing?

Step 7 Edit

W.2.5: With guidance and support from adults and peers, focus on a topic and strengthen writing as needed by . . . editing.

L.2.2c: Use an apostrophe to form contractions . . . .

FOCUS Contractions

Modeled Instruction

One way to make your writing sound friendly is to use contractions. A **contraction** is two words put together. An apostrophe takes the place of the missing letters. Here are some examples.

Language Handbook To learn more about contractions, turn to page 212.

Forming Contractions					
Two Words	does not	do not	let us	I would	it is
Contraction	doesn't	don't	let's	I'd	it's

Read part of Luke's draft below.

MENTOR TEXT Draft

It would be harder because we don't get snow and ice here. I live in Florida. We might get a little bit of snow sometimes. But it is not enough snow to build igloos.

1 **Circle** the contraction in the first sentence. **Write** the two words that make the contraction.

_____

2 **Read** the last sentence. Help Luke make a contraction.

_____

Guided Practice

Circle the words that can be made into contractions.
Write the contractions on the lines.

---

3 The tree house does not hurt the tree.

> **HINT** The first word in the contraction does not change.

_____

---

4 They do not need to use wood from trees.

_____

---

5 It is one way to live while riding on the water.

> **HINT** The apostrophe takes the place of the missing letters.

_____

Independent Practice

 Write Time Check that you used contractions correctly. Check your spelling, capitalization, and punctuation, also.

Turn and Talk
How can contractions help your writing?

W.2.6: With guidance and support from adults . . . produce and publish writing, including in collaboration with peers.

Step 8 Publish and Share

FOCUS Ask and Answer Questions

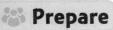 Prepare

Get ready to share! You can show that you are interested in what others have written by **asking a question.**

Here is one question about an unusual home. How would you answer it?

Question

What is the best thing about that home?

Answer

Share

Write two questions you might be asked about the unusual home you chose. Then **write** answers to those questions.

Question

HINT Think about the things that make the home special and different.

Answer

Question

HINT What questions did you think of when you first read about the home?

Answer

Independent Practice

 Write Your Opinion Paragraph

Which home would be the most fun for a weekend visit?

Writing a Narrative: Diary

W.2.3: Write narratives in which they recount a well elaborated event or short sequence of events, include details to describe actions, thoughts, and feelings, use temporal words to signal event order, and provide a sense of closure.

Step 1 Learn About Narrative Writing

What Is Narrative Writing?

A narrative tells a made-up or a real story. The characters can be people or plants, animals, and objects that behave like people.

Narrative Writing has:

- a **beginning** that introduces the characters and setting

- a **middle** that shows how the characters think, feel, and act

- an **end** that finishes the story and makes sense

Kin wrote one type of narrative. He wrote a diary that tells the events in a lizard's day. Let's read it.

MENTOR TEXT

September 6, 2015

Today was a great day to be a lizard. When I first woke up, I was shivering. It gets really cold in the desert at night. Right away, I crawled up on a flat rock in the sunlight to warm up.

Then I noticed I was really hungry. I needed some breakfast! I saw a big meaty bug creeping slowly nearby, and I thought that would make a delicious meal. My tan skin helped me blend in with the sand, so the poor bug never saw me. I quickly stuck out my long, sticky, tongue and caught that bug! It was so juicy and tasty!

Next it was time to explore. I crawled slowly toward a tall cactus to look around. Suddenly, I saw a shadow. I was scared, so I raced up the cactus to hide on a tan patch. The hawk couldn't find me! I was tired, but I was safe.

After a while I headed home. It was a day full of adventures, and I can't wait to do this all again tomorrow.

1 Read the **beginning**. **Underline** the character and setting in green.

2 Read the **middle**. **Underline** facts about the lizard in yellow.

3 Read the **middle**. **Circle** words that tell how the lizard feels in yellow.

4 Read the **end**. **Underline** words that finish the diary in red.

W.2.7: Participate in shared research and writing projects.

Step 2 Unpack Your Assignment

FOCUS Identify Assignment Details

Modeled Instruction

Let's see how Kin unpacks his assignment.

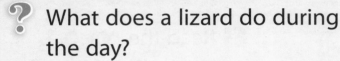

Kin's Assignment

? What does a lizard do during the day?

📖 Read two articles about lizards.

✏️ Imagine that you are a lizard living in the desert. Write a diary for your parents about your day.

- In the **beginning** introduce yourself and the setting.
- In the **middle** descibe what you thought, felt, and did during the day. Include at least three facts about lizards.
- Tell what happened at the **end**.

Think Aloud

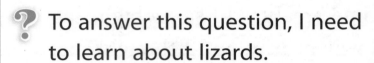

? To answer this question, I need to learn about lizards.

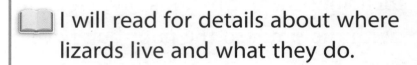

📖 I will read for details about where lizards live and what they do.

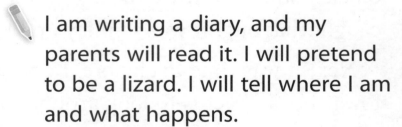

✏️ I am writing a diary, and my parents will read it. I will pretend to be a lizard. I will tell where I am and what happens.

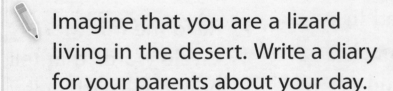

Let's read and mark your assignment.

Write Time

Your Assignment

? What does a shark do during the day?

📖 Read *Amazing Sharks!* and "Shark Bites."

✏️ Imagine that you're a shark living in the ocean. Write a diary for your friends about your day.

- In the **beginning** introduce yourself and the setting.
- In the **middle** describe what you thought, felt, and did during the day. Include at least three facts about sharks.
- Tell what happened at the **end**.

1 **Underline** the question you will answer.

2 **Draw a box** around what you will write.

3 **Circle** who will read what you write.

Turn and Talk
What should the beginning, middle, and end of your diary include?

W.2.8: Recall information from experiences or gather information from provided sources to answer a question.

Step 3 Read and Gather Evidence

Source Text 1

from

Amazing Sharks!

by Sarah L. Thomson

The great white shark is named for its white belly.

1   There are more than 350 different kinds of sharks. Some are as long as a fire truck. Some are so small you could hold one in your hand. Some sharks have dull teeth. Others have teeth so sharp they can take a bite out of a turtle's shell. Some sharks live in rivers. Others hide on the ocean bottom or swim in deep water. Some sharks even glow in the dark.

2   Almost all sharks are hunters. Animals that hunt are called predators. The white shark is a predator. It attacks from below to kill its favorite food—seals or sea lions. These animals are called its prey. Sharks are fish, but they are different from other fish. Other fish have bones. A shark's skeleton is cartilage. Your ears and nose are made of cartilage. It bends more easily than bone. A shark can bend and twist to turn quickly when it is swimming.

3   Some sharks eat stingrays or spiny sea urchins. Many eat other sharks. Tiger sharks have eaten tin cans and metal wire! Sharks have rows and rows of teeth. If one tooth falls out, a bigger one moves up to fill in the hole. Some sharks lose thousands of teeth during their lives.

▲ A tiger shark's teeth are shaped to cut and saw.

Vision
100 meters

Hearing
1,000 meters

▶ A shark can hear ten times farther than it can see.

4   Sharks have many senses to help them find food. A shark can hear a fish in the water from more than a mile away. It can smell one drop of blood in a million drops of water.

▲

A lemon shark feels electricity from food hiding in the sand.

5   If a fish is swimming or splashing, a shark can feel the water moving. Sharks can also feel electricity. Every living thing gives off a little bit of electricity. People cannot feel it. But sharks can. Even if prey is hiding, a shark can still find it by feeling electricity in the water.

6   Many people are afraid of sharks. But most sharks leave people alone. You are more likely to be hit by lightning than to be killed by a shark.

7   Sharks are important to life in the ocean.

Shark Bites

A baby shark is called a *pup*.

Shark pups swim away after they are born. They can take care of themselves.

A group of sharks can be called a *school*, a *frenzy*, a *shiver*, or a *herd*.

Sharks are *carnivores*. They eat animals like fish, crabs, and seals.

Sharks look for bright colors and shiny things as they swim.

Think It Through

Answer these questions. Use details from *Amazing Sharks!* and "Shark Bites."

1 What is special about a shark's body?

HINT Many sharks share the same traits.

2 Where do sharks live?

HINT Reread page 98 of *Amazing Sharks!*

3 How do sharks find food?

HINT Look for verbs that show sharks using their senses.

4 What do sharks eat?

HINT Look for these details in both sources.

Step 4 Plan

 Modeled Instruction

Kin made a plan before he wrote. He thought about how the lizard thought, felt, and acted during the day.

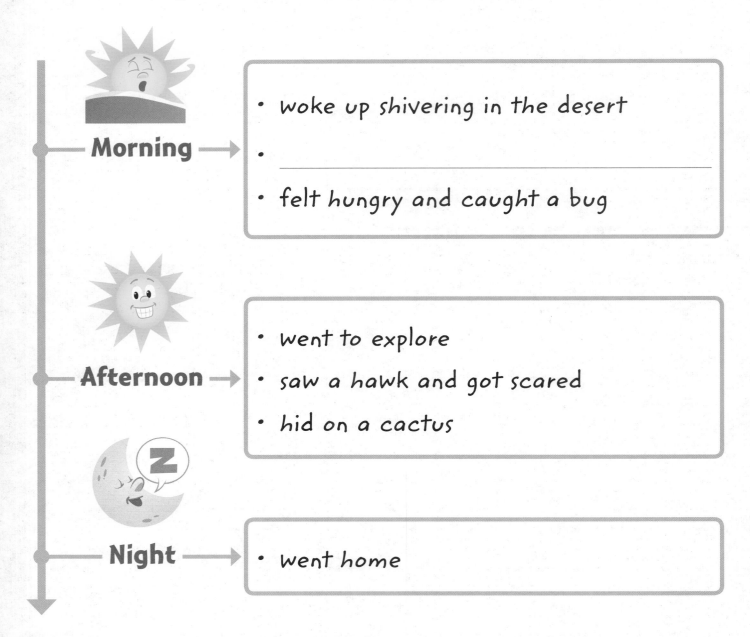

Morning →
- woke up shivering in the desert
- _____
- felt hungry and caught a bug

Afternoon →
- went to explore
- saw a hawk and got scared
- hid on a cactus

Night →
- went home

1 **Add** a detail that tells what happened in the morning.

Use the time line below to plan your writing.

2 **Write** about each part of the shark's day. Think about how the shark thought, felt, and acted.

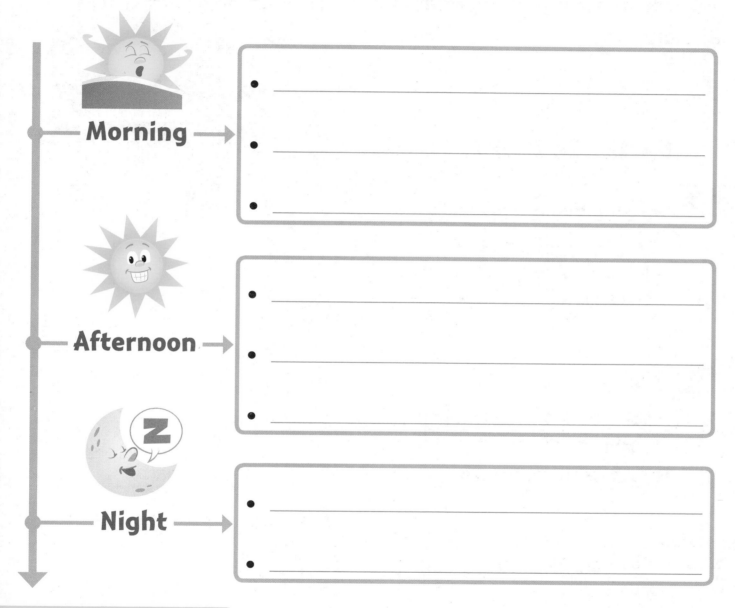

Morning →

Afternoon →

Night →

Write Time Write a sentence telling the most exciting part of the shark's day.

W.2.3: Write narratives in which they recount a well elaborated event . . .

Step 5 Draft

This chart shows the parts of a narrative. Use the ideas here as you draft the beginning, middle, and end of your diary.

Parts of a Diary

BEGINNING	A strong **beginning** should:
Introduces characters and setting	• Tell **who** is in the story. • Tell **where** and **when** the story takes place.

MIDDLE	**Middle** sentences should:
Describes the events	• Use details to describe how the characters **think, feel,** and **act.** • Tell the events **in order.**

END	The **end** of your story should:
Tells how the story ends	• Make **sense.** • Make the story feel **finished.**

Write the BEGINNING

Study the beginning of Kin's diary. Then try writing the beginning of your diary.

BEGINNING

MIDDLE

END

MENTOR TEXT

Today was a great day to be a lizard. When I first woke up, I was shivering. It gets really cold in the desert at night. Right away, I crawled up on a flat rock in the sunlight to warm up.

1 **Circle** the character Kin is writing about.

2 **Underline** the setting.

MY DIARY

3 **Write** a sentence to introduce your character and setting.

_____

_____

HINT Remember that you are pretending to be the character.

Independent Practice

 Write Time Draft the beginning of your diary. Use the tips from the chart on page 106.

Turn and Talk What should your reader find out in the beginning?

W.2.3: Write narratives in which they recount a well elaborated event . . . include details to describe actions, thoughts, and feelings . . . and provide a sense of closure.

Write the MIDDLE

Read to see how Kin included the lizard's actions in his diary. Then try writing some of the shark's actions.

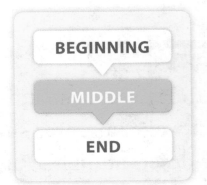

MENTOR TEXT

> Next it was time to explore. I climbed slowly toward a tall cactus to look around. Suddenly, I saw a shadow. I was scared, so I raced up the cactus to hide on a tan patch. The hawk couldn't find me! I was tired, but I was safe.

1 **Underline** two of the lizard's actions.

MY DIARY

2 **Write** a sentence describing one of your shark's actions.

_____

_____

_____

> **HINT** Look at your time line on page 105.

Write the END

Study the end of Kin's diary. Then try writing the end of your diary.

BEGINNING

MIDDLE

END

⭐ **MENTOR TEXT**

> After a while I headed home. It was a day full of adventures, and I can't wait to do this all again tomorrow.

1 **Underline** the sentence that makes the lizard's day feel finished.

✏️ **MY DIARY**

2 **Write** a sentence that makes your shark's day feel finished.

HINT What do you do at the end of a day?

_____

_____

_____

👤 Independent Practice

 Write Time Finish drafting the middle and end of your diary.

Turn and Talk 💬
What are some ways to finish a story?

W.2.5: With guidance and support from adults and peers, focus on a topic and strengthen writing as needed by revising . . .

Step 6 Revise

FOCUS Details

Modeled Instruction

Let's read part of Kin's draft and part of his checklist.

> **MENTOR TEXT** Draft
>
> Then I noticed I was really hungry. I needed some breakfast! I saw a big meaty bug creeping slowly nearby, and I thought that would make a delicious meal. The bug never saw me. I quickly caught that bug! It was so juicy and tasty!

Narrative Writing Checklist

✔ Did I tell how the characters think, feel, and act?

✔ Did I include facts about lizards?

1 **Underline** details that show what the lizard is thinking or feeling.

2 Where could Kin add facts about lizards?

_____

_____

_____

Guided Practice

> I wrote about a shark's day. Can you help me make this part of my diary better?

> I'm very tired! It's hard being Sandy the Shark in this big ocean. I caught a lobster today. Then I swam after a fish, but it got away. One of my teeth fell out.

3 **Underline** details that show what the shark is thinking or feeling.

HINT Look for words that show emotions.

4 Where could Hershel add facts about sharks?

_____

_____

_____

Independent Practice

Write Time Use the Narrative Writing Checklist to help you revise your writing.

Turn and Talk
Where could Hershel add more thoughts and feelings to his draft?

L.2.1e: Use adjectives and adverbs, and choose between them depending on what is to be modified.

FOCUS Add Adjectives and Adverbs

 Modeled Instruction

You can improve your diary by adding **adjectives** and **adverbs**. These can help you make your descriptions clear and interesting.

Adjectives tell about nouns.	The shark saw a **shiny can**.
	The **gigantic shark** swallowed a fish.
Adverbs tell about verbs.	The shark **raced quickly** toward the seal.
	The fish **swam nervously** away from the shark.

Let's see how Kin used adjectives and adverbs in his diary.

MENTOR TEXT

I needed some breakfast! I saw a big, meaty bug creeping slowly nearby, and I thought that would make a delicious meal.

Think Aloud

- The adverb *slowly* tells how the bug was creeping.

- The adjectives *big* and *meaty* help my readers picture the bug. The adjective *delicious* describes how much I would like to eat it!

Guided Practice

Circle the adjective or adverb that adds the correct detail to each sentence.

1 The (hungry, large) lizard looked around the rocks for a bug.

HINT Which adjective tells how the lizard is feeling?

2 A hawk screeched (loudly, bright) in the sky.

3 The lizard stood (fast, still) and waited.

HINT The word *waited* gives a clue about how the lizard stood.

4 The lizard crawled onto the cactus and felt its (sharp, yellow) thorns.

5 The (rough, chilly) lizard shivered in the cold.

Independent Practice

Write Time Try adding adjectives and adverbs to your diary.

Turn and Talk
How do adjectives and adverbs improve your writing?

Step 7 Edit

W.2.5: With guidance and support from adults and peers, focus on a topic and strengthen writing as needed by . . . editing.

L.2.1f: Produce, expand, and rearrange complete simple and compound sentences.

FOCUS Compound Sentences

Modeled Instruction

A **compound sentence** is two simple sentences joined together. Words such as **and**, **but**, **or**, and **so** join sentences. A comma usually comes before these joining words.

Language Handbook To learn more about compound sentences, turn to page 206.

Simple Sentences	Compound Sentences
A lizard eats flies. It also eats spiders.	A lizard eats flies, **and** it also eats spiders.
A lizard eats bugs. It only eats live bugs.	A lizard eats bugs, **but** it only eats live bugs.

Read part of Kin's draft below.

MENTOR TEXT Draft

I was scared, so I raced up the cactus to hide on a tan patch. The hawk couldn't find me! I was tired. I was safe.

1 **Circle** the joining word Kin used.

2 **Read** the last two sentences. Help Kin make a compound sentence.

_____

_____

Write a compound sentence by joining each pair of simple sentences.

3 The shark was hungry. It ate fifty fish.

_____

_____

> **HINT** Remember to include a comma before the joining word.

4 The turtle swam fast. The shark took a bite of its shell.

_____

_____

5 A shark can swim in a straight line. It can bend and twist as it swims.

_____

_____

> **HINT** Can the shark swim straight and bend at the same time?

Independent Practice

Write Time Check that you wrote compound sentences correctly. Check your spelling, capitalization, and punctuation, also.

Turn and Talk
How can you decide which joining word to use?

W.2.6: With guidance and support from adults . . . produce and publish writing, including in collaboration with peers.

Step 8 Publish and Share

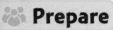 **Prepare**

Put on a puppet show to retell your shark's day! **Write** the names of two characters you will use in your puppet show. Then **write** some things each character might say.

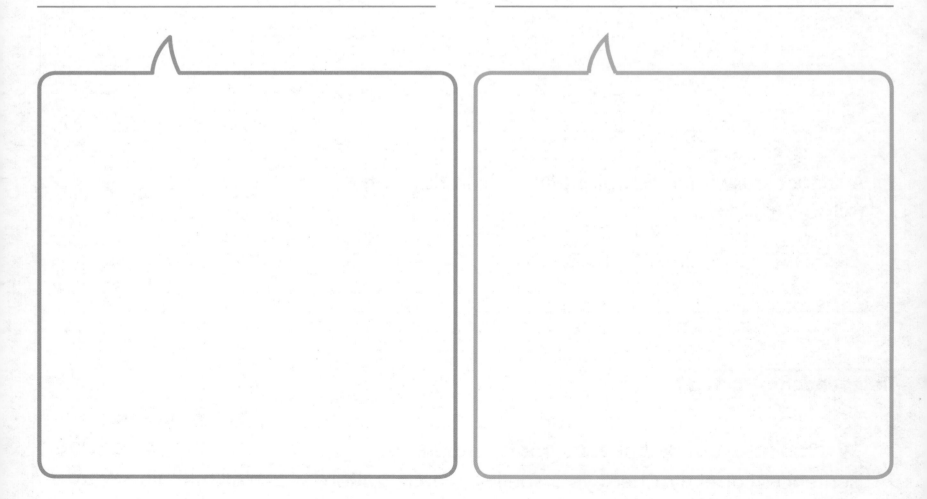

Draw your setting below. Then use your puppets and setting to bring your diary to life.

Independent Practice

 **Write Your Diary**

What does a shark do during the day?

W.2.2: Write informative/explanatory texts in which they introduce a topic, use facts and definitions to develop points, and provide a concluding statement or section.

Writing to Inform: Lab Report

Step 1 Learn About Informational Writing

What Is Informational Writing?

Informational writing uses facts to tell about something real. Writers explain what something is or how something works.

Informational Writing has:

- a **beginning** that introduces the topic
- a **middle** that tells facts and details about the topic
- an **end** that sums up the information

Lea wrote an informational text. She did an experiment and then wrote a lab report to explain the results. Let's read it.

©Curriculum Associates, LLC   Copying is not permitted.

MENTOR TEXT

Lifting with a Lever
by Lea Dobbs

How can you make objects easier to lift? I did an experiment to find out. I gathered a lever, a fulcrum, and an object. I used a yardstick as a lever, the part that moves up and down. I used a block as a fulcrum. The fulcrum supports the lever. The object I lifted was a book. I wanted to find out where I should move the fulcrum to make the book easier to lift.

First, I put the fulcrum near my hand. I placed the book on the other end of the yardstick, and I pushed down on the lever. The end of the lever closest to me was very short. It was hard to lift the book.

Next, I put the fulcrum far away from my hand. This way, the part of the lever closest to me was longer. When I pushed down, it was much easier to lift the book.

The results were clear. Using a lever and fulcrum can make objects easier to lift. The best way is to move the fulcrum close to the object you want to lift. When the lever is long on the opposite side of the object, the object feels lighter.

1 Lea introduces her experiment in the **beginning. Underline** two sentences that tell what she wants to find out in green.

2 Lea tells about her experiment in the **middle. Underline** two details that explain what she tried in yellow.

3 Lea sums up her results at the **end. Underline** the sentences that tell her results in red.

W.2.7: Participate in shared research and writing projects (e.g., . . . record science observations).

Step 2 Unpack Your Assignment

FOCUS Identify Assignment Details

Modeled Instruction

Let's see how Lea unpacks her assignment.

Lea's Assignment

❓ How can you make an object easier to lift?

📖 Read a science article about a lever and fulcrum.

✏️ Do an experiment. Then write a lab report for a science fair. Explain your experiment and the results.

- In the **beginning** tell what you wanted to find out and what materials you used.
- In the **middle** explain what you tried and what happened.
- Draw a conclusion about the results at the **end**.

Think Aloud

❓ This question tells me what I need to find out. I will answer it when I do my experiment.

📖 I will find out what a lever and fulcrum are, and how they work. I need to explain this in my lab report.

✏️ I am writing a lab report for a science fair. I will include what my experiment is, what I did, what happened, and the conclusions I drew.

Let's read and mark your assignment.

Write Time

Your Assignment

? How can you change the speed of a vehicle?

📖 Read *Wheels* and "How to Build a Bottle Car."

✏️ Do an experiment. Then write a lab report for your classmates. Explain your experiment and the results.

- In the **beginning** tell what you wanted to find out and what materials you used.

- In the **middle** explain what you tried and what happened.

- Draw a conclusion about the results at the **end**.

1 **Underline** the question you will answer.

2 **Draw a box** around what you will write.

3 **Circle** who will read what you write.

Turn and Talk
How is a lab report different from a story?

W.2.8: Recall information from experiences or gather information from provided sources to answer a question.

Step 3 Read and Gather Evidence

Source Text 1

from

Wheels

by David and Patricia Armentrout

wheel

axle

1   Wheels are familiar to all of us. Look around; they are everywhere. Bicycles, cars, and even vacuum cleaners have wheels. Everyone uses them, but what do you really know about wheels? For starters, they are round. Wheels also come in many sizes: big wheels, small wheels, fat wheels, and skinny wheels.

2   To be a true machine, a wheel needs an axle. An **axle** is a shaft or rod in the center of a wheel. The wheel turns on the axle. An axle can also connect two wheels so they can work together. How can wheels and axles make our work easier?

Mechanical Advantage

3   Wheels and axles, as with all simple machines, have one thing in common. They make our work easier by giving us a **mechanical advantage**. A person using a simple machine can do the same amount of work with less effort. Most everyone would agree that's a big advantage.

4   For example, let's say it's your job to harvest pumpkins from the garden. Can you drag them across the ground? Maybe, but they are heavy. What could you use to make your work easier? Try loading the pumpkins into a wheelbarrow. It is easier to use a wheelbarrow than it is to drag the pumpkins. A wheelbarrow has a wheel and axle to share the weight, also called the load. The wheel and axle gives you a mechanical advantage.

Wheels and Friction

5   When two objects rub against each other, they create **friction**. Friction slows movement.

6   Imagine dragging a garbage can down the driveway. The can scrapes noisily along as you pull. The noise comes from friction between the bottom of the can and the driveway.

7   The more friction there is, the harder it is to pull the can. Would wheels make the job easier? You bet. It is easier to roll a heavy object than it is to drag it along. Wheels reduce friction.

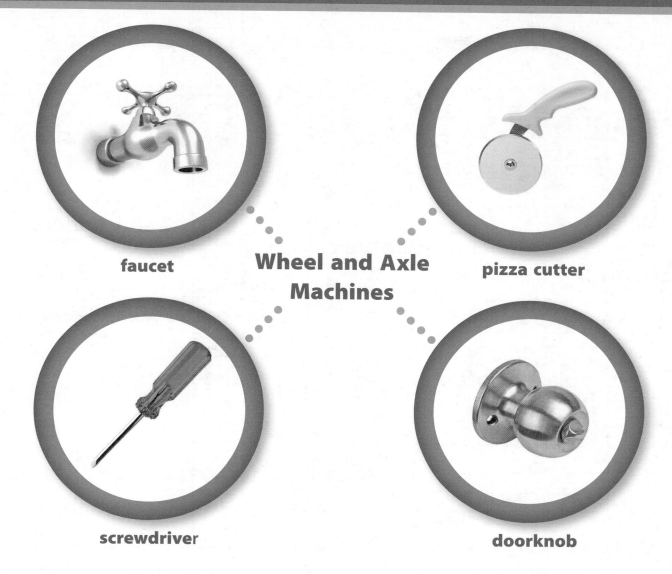

faucet

Wheel and Axle Machines

pizza cutter

screwdriver

doorknob

Useful Machines

8   Machines like the wheel and axle make our lives easier. Sometimes they show up in the most unexpected places. For example, did you know the screwdriver is a wheel and axle? The handle acts as the wheel when it is turned. The shaft is the axle.

9   Think about how doorknobs, pizza cutters, and faucet handles work. Take a walk around your home and see how many useful wheels you can find.

How to Build a BOTTLE CAR

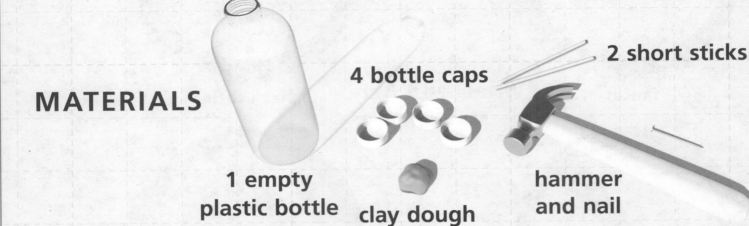

MATERIALS

1 empty
plastic bottle

4 bottle caps

clay dough

hammer
and nail

2 short sticks

STEPS

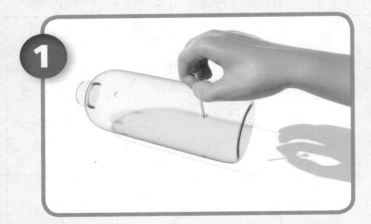

1 **Prepare the axles.** Ask an adult to make two holes on each side of the bottle, using the nail. The holes should line up.

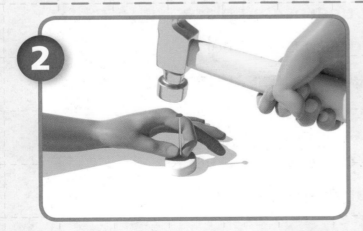

2 **Prepare the wheels.** Ask an adult to make a hole in the center of each cap, using the hammer and nail.

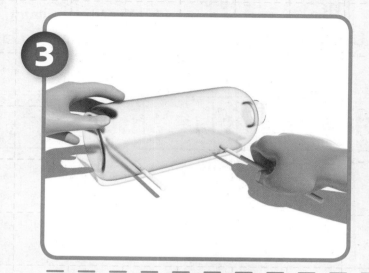

Insert the axles. Slide a short stick through the holes on each end of the bottle.

Add the wheels. Slide a cap onto each short stick. Use the clay dough to hold it in place.

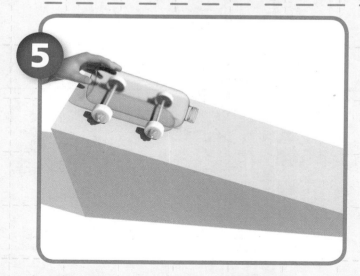

Make it go! Place your car on a ramp and watch it go. Experiment with ways to make it go faster or slower.

Think It Through

1 **Draw** and **label** each of your materials. Then **write** a sentence telling how it will be used in your experiment.

HINT What will you use to make the car go faster or slower?

Materials	How They Will Be Used

2 **Write** two changes that would make your bottle car go faster or slower. Then **write** what you think will happen. See the example below.

Change: _Take off the wheels._

Possible result: _This will make more friction and make the car go slower._

• •

Change: _____

Possible result: _____

_____

• •

Change: _____

Possible result: _____

_____

W.2.2: Write informative/explanatory texts in which they . . . use facts . . . to develop points. . . .

Step 4 Plan

FOCUS Organize Your Details

Modeled Instruction

Lea did her experiment. She wrote what happened when she moved the fulcrum.

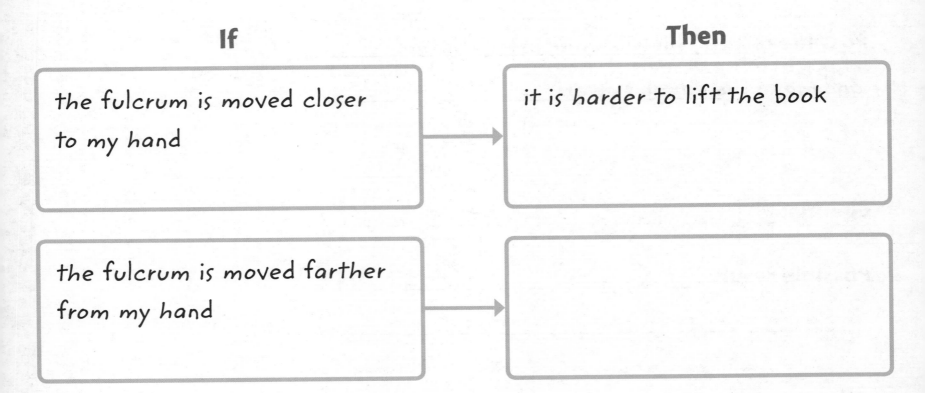

If	Then
the fulcrum is moved closer to my hand	it is harder to lift the book
the fulcrum is moved farther from my hand	

1 **Fill in** what happened when Lea moved the fulcrum farther from her hand.

Now write the results from your experiment.

2 **Fill in** the "If" column with the change you planned.

3 **Fill in** the "Then" column with the results.

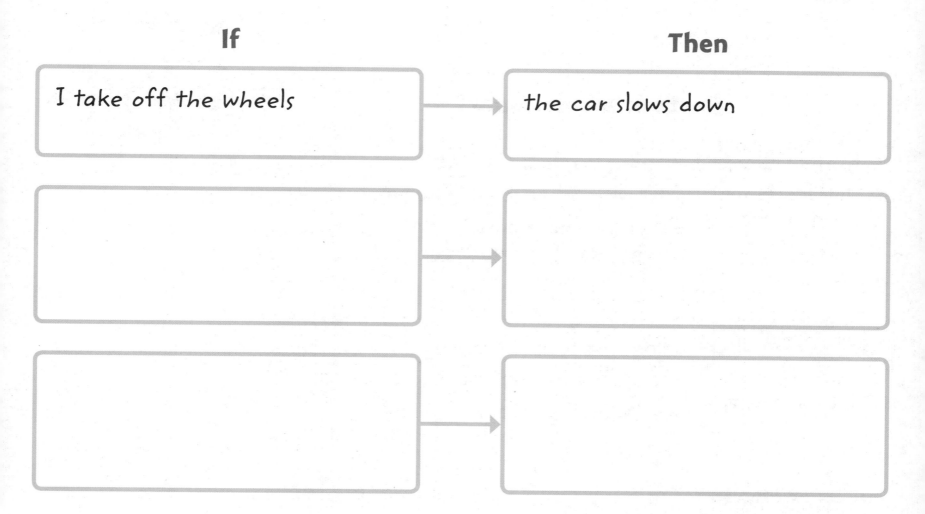

If	Then
I take off the wheels	the car slows down

Independent Practice

 Write Time Draw a conclusion about your experiment. Were any results different than you expected?

W.2.2: Write informative/explanatory texts in which they introduce a topic . . .

Step 5 Draft

This chart shows the parts of a lab report. Use the ideas here as you draft your **beginning**, **middle**, and **end**.

Parts of a Lab Report

| BEGINNING | A strong **beginning** should: |
| Introduces the experiment | • Tell what you wanted to **find out.**
• Describe your **materials,** giving **definitions** for new words. |

| MIDDLE | **Middle** paragraphs should: |
| Describes the experiment | • Describe **each step** in the experiment.
• Tell **what happened.** |

| END | The **end** of your lab report should: |
| Explains the results | • **Sum up** the experiment.
• **Draw a conclusion** about the results. |

Write the BEGINNING

Study the beginning of Lea's lab report. Then try writing the beginning of your lab report.

BEGINNING

MIDDLE

END

⭐ **MENTOR TEXT**

How can you make objects easier to lift? I did an experiment to find out. I gathered a lever, a fulcrum, and an object. I used a yardstick as a lever, the part that moves up and down. I used a block as a fulcrum. The fulcrum supports the lever. The object I lifted was a book. I wanted to find out where I should move the fulcrum to make the book easier to lift.

1 **Circle** the question that introduces the experiment.

2 **Underline** the sentences that describe the materials.

✏️ **MY LAB REPORT**

3 **Write** a sentence that introduces your experiment.

HINT What were you trying to find out?

_____

_____

👤 **Independent Practice**

 Write Time Draft the beginning of your lab report.

💬 **Turn and Talk**
What should your beginning explain?

W.2.2: . . . use facts and definitions to develop points, and provide a concluding statement or section.

Write the MIDDLE

Read about the first change in Lea's experiment. Then write about your first change.

BEGINNING

MIDDLE

END

⭐ MENTOR TEXT

First, I put the fulcrum near my hand. I placed the book on the other end of the yardstick, and I pushed down on the lever. The end of the lever closest to me was very short. It was hard to lift the book.

1 Draw a box around the change that Lea made.

2 Underline Lea's results.

✏ MY LAB REPORT

3 Write the first change you made. Tell your results.

_____

_____

_____

HINT Use the chart on page 137 to remember your changes and results.

Write the END

Study the end of Lea's lab report. Then try writing the end of your lab report.

BEGINNING
↓
MIDDLE
↓
END

⭐ MENTOR TEXT

The results were clear. Using a lever and fulcrum can make objects easier to lift. The best way is to move the fulcrum close to the object you want to lift. When the lever is long on the opposite side of the object, the object feels lighter.

1 **Underline** the sentence where Lea draws a conclusion about her results.

✏️ MY LAB REPORT

2 **Write** a sentence that draws a conclusion about your results.

> **HINT** What did you find out?

_____

_____

_____

👤 Independent Practice

 Write Time Draft the middle and end of your lab report. Use the tips from the chart on page 138.

💬 Turn and Talk

How does your ending connect to your beginning?

W.2.5: With guidance and support from adults and peers, focus on a topic and strengthen writing as needed by revising . . .

Step 6 Revise

Modeled Instruction

Let's read part of Lea's draft and part of her checklist.

MENTOR TEXT Draft

> First I put the fulcrum near my hand. I put the yardstick on the fulcrum. Then I put the book on the other end of the yardstick. I pushed down on the lever to lift the book. Next I put the fulcrum far from my hand. I pushed down on the lever again.

Informational Writing Checklist

✔ Did I describe each step of my experiment?

✔ Did I tell what happened at each step?

1 **Underline** the two places where Lea put the fulcrum.

2 How can Lea improve her lab report?

_____

_____

_____

I wrote about my experiment. Can you help me make this part of my lab report better?

I made changes to my bottle car to see if it would go faster or slower. I made the first change to one car and then raced it against a car that I didn't change. The car that I changed went faster.

3 **Underline** what happened after Hershel's first change.

4 What information did Hershel leave out of his paragraph?

_____

_____

Independent Practice

Write Time Use the Informational Writing Checklist to help you revise your writing.

Turn and Talk
Why does Hershel need the information he left out?

Modeled Instruction

One way to help readers understand your writing is to give definitions and context clues that explain new or challenging words. These may be in the same sentence as the new word or in nearby sentences.

A **definition** tells the meaning of a word.

A **context clue** gives a hint about the word's meaning.

Let's see how Lea used definitions and context clues in her lab report.

MENTOR TEXT

I gathered a lever, a fulcrum, and an object. I used a yardstick as a lever, the part that moves up and down. I used a block as a fulcrum. The fulcrum supports the lever. The object I lifted was a book.

Think Aloud

- I wasn't sure my readers would know the word *lever*, so I gave a definition.

- I had never heard the word *fulcrum*, so I didn't think my readers would know it. I gave a context clue to explain it.

Guided Practice

Let's check a different part of my draft for definitions and context clues.

I made my bottle car by adding two axles and four wheels. An axle is what connects the wheels. Then I used a ramp five times to make sure that the car worked.

---

1 **Underline** the definition Hershel gave for the word *axle*.

> **HINT** A definition tells what the word means.

2 **Write** a context clue to help readers understand the word *ramp*.

_____

_____

> **HINT** Context clues give hints about the meaning.

Independent Practice

 Write Time Add definitions and context clues to new or challenging words in your lab report.

Turn and Talk
How can definitions and context clues make your writing clear?

Step 7 Edit

W.2.5: With guidance and support from adults and peers, focus on a topic and strengthen writing as needed by . . . editing.

L.2.2e: Consult reference materials, including beginning dictionaries, as needed to check and correct spellings.

FOCUS Spelling

Modeled Instruction

Before you publish your lab report, be sure you spelled all the words correctly. Use a **dictionary** to check a word's spelling.

The words in a dictionary are in the same order as the letters of the alphabet. They are arranged alphabetically.

Read part of Lea's draft below.

> **Language Handbook**
> To learn more about using a dictionary to check spelling, turn to page 218.

MENTOR TEXT Draft

I decided to do an experimant with a lever to find out. First I gathered the supplies I would need. I used a yardstik as a lever. The lever is the part that moves up and down.

1 **Use a dictionary** to check the spelling of *experimant*. If it is incorrect, cross out the word and write the correct spelling.

_____

2 **Cross out** another misspelled word. **Write** the correct spelling.

_____

Guided Practice

Circle words that are spelled incorrectly.
Write the correct spelling of the words on the lines.

3 I placed the fulcrum as far away as possibel.

_____

HINT Use a dictionary to spell the word correctly.

4 The objict I lifted was a book.

_____

5 It is easeir to lift things with a levar.

_____

HINT More than one word in a sentence may be misspelled.

6 Push down on the opossite side of the wieght.

_____

Independent Practice

 Write Time Check the spelling, capitalization, and punctuation in your lab report.

Turn and Talk
Why is it important to spell words correctly?

W.2.6: With guidance and support from adults . . . produce and publish writing, including in collaboration with peers.

Step 8 Publish and Share

FOCUS Ask for Clarification

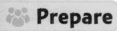 **Prepare**

Listen to your classmates as they share the results of their experiment. Is there anything that is not clear? If so, ask questions to **clarify,** or get more information.

Here is one question you could ask to clarify a change to the bottle car.

Question

How did you add weight to the car?

Share

Write two questions you would ask about a classmate's experiment. Then **write** your classmate's response.

Question

HINT Ask yourself what you don't understand about your classmate's experiment.

Answer

Question

HINT Contrast your results with your classmate's. What was different?

Answer

Independent Practice

 Write Your Lab Report

How can you change the speed of a vehicle?

W.2.1: Write opinion pieces in which they introduce the topic or book they are writing about, state an opinion, supply reasons that support the opinion, use linking words (e.g., *because, and, also*) to connect opinion and reasons, and provide a concluding statement or section.

Lesson 6
Writing an Opinion: Letter

Step 1 Learn About Opinion Writing

What Is Opinion Writing?

An opinion tells what we like or what we would choose. In opinion writing, writers tell their opinion and give reasons to support it. Sometimes they try to convince readers to agree with them.

Opinion Writing has:

- a **beginning** that introduces the topic and opinion
- a **middle** that gives reasons
- an **end** that asks the reader to take action.

Danna wrote a letter to her principal, Mrs. Wadi. Her letter tells which author her class wants to be a guest speaker. Let's read it.

MENTOR TEXT

April 23, 2015

Dear Mrs. Wadi,

I am writing to say that Adam Bean should be our guest speaker for Author Day. Adam Bean is my favorite author. I think he would be a great guest speaker. I hope you will agree.

Adam Bean writes funny stories. In *Dog Gone*, Jack starts a dog-washing business. But he doesn't know that dogs hate baths! The nervous dogs race around wildly trying to escape, and Jack falls into the tub. The only one who gets a bath is Jack!

Adam Bean also gives kids like us great tips on how to write stories. He says to write what we know. So we write about school, brothers and sisters, pets, and funny things that happen. We try to make our stories just like his.

Adam Bean would be the best guest speaker. He writes funny stories and could help us to be better writers. Please invite Adam Bean to be our guest speaker on Author Day. You will not be sorry.

Sincerely,

Danna Cortez

1 Read the **beginning**. **Underline** Danna's opinion in green.

2 Read the **middle**. **Underline** Danna's reasons in yellow.

3 Read the **end**. **Underline** the words that tell Danna's reader to take action.

W.2.7: Participate in shared research and writing projects.

Step 2 Unpack Your Assignment

FOCUS Identify Assignment Details

Modeled Instruction

Let's see how Danna unpacks her assignment.

Danna's Assignment

? Who should be our guest speaker on Author Day?

📖 Review several books by Adam Bean and Marta Kozuli.

✏ Write a letter to your principal. Share your opinion about which author should be invited.

- In the **beginning** tell the topic and your opinion.
- Give at least two reasons in the **middle** that tell why.
- Ask your reader to take action at the **end**.

Think Aloud

? To answer this question, I need to decide what I like about Adam Bean and Marta Kozuli.

📖 I will decide what each author does well as I review their books.

✏ I am writing a letter to my principal. I will tell my topic and my opinion. I will give at least two reasons and ask my principal to invite the speaker I choose.

Let's read and mark your assignment.

Write Time

Your Assignment

? Which story would second graders enjoy reading?

📖 Read "The Boy Who Cried 'Wolf!'" and "The Boy Who Cried 'Alien!'"

✏️ Write a letter to your school librarian. Share your opinion about which story you would choose.

- In the **beginning** tell the topic and your opinion.
- Give at least two reasons in the **middle** that tell why.
- Ask your reader to take action at the **end**.

1 **Underline** the question you will answer.

2 **Draw a box** around what you will write.

3 **Circle** who will read what you write.

Turn and Talk
What is important about each part of your letter?

W.2.8: Recall information from experiences or gather information from provided sources to answer a question.

Step 3 Read and Gather Evidence

Source Text 1

The Boy Who Cried "Wolf!"

=== an Aesop fable ===

1 There once was a boy who lived near a tiny village. This boy was a shepherd. His job was to watch over the sheep and keep them safe from hungry wolves. Father told the boy that if he saw a wolf, he should call out loudly and the villagers would come to help him scare away the wolf.

2 Every day, all day long, the boy watched the sheep. After a while, he found life in the pasture to be very dull and tiresome. One day, he thought of a way to amuse himself.

3 The boy ran toward the village shouting, "Wolf! Wolf!"

4   As he expected, the villagers dropped their work and ran quickly to the pasture. But when they got there they found the boy rolling on the ground with laughter. There was no hungry wolf. He had played a trick on them.

5   The next day, the boy decided to play the trick again. He shouted, "Wolf! Wolf!" Again the villagers ran to help him, and again the boy laughed at them.

6   Then one evening as the sun was setting, the boy noticed a real wolf stalking his sheep. In terror the boy ran toward the village shouting, "Wolf! Wolf!" But the villagers did not come to help him as they had before. "He cannot fool us again," they said. As a result, all of the boy's sheep ran away.

7   The boy realized that what happened was his fault. He had lied so many times that no one believed him anymore, even when he told the truth.

Think It Through

1 **Fill in** each chart. Use details from "The Boy Who Cried 'Wolf!'" and "The Boy Who Cried 'Alien!'"

How are the stories alike?

HINT What do the boys do? What do they learn?

How are the stories different?

The Boy Who Cried "Wolf!"	The Boy Who Cried "Alien!"

HINT Think about the characters and setting.

2 Which story do you think second graders would enjoy reading more? **Circle** your answer.

HINT Which story do you like better? Do you think other kids would like it, too?

The Boy Who Cried "Wolf!"

The Boy Who Cried "Alien!"

3 Why would second graders enjoy that story? **Write** two reasons.

HINT A reason explains why you have your opinion.

_____

_____

_____

_____

_____

W.2.1: . . . state an opinion, supply reasons that support the opinion . . .

Step 4 Plan

FOCUS Organize Your Details

Modeled Instruction

Danna made a plan before she wrote. She thought about why Adam Bean would be a great guest speaker.

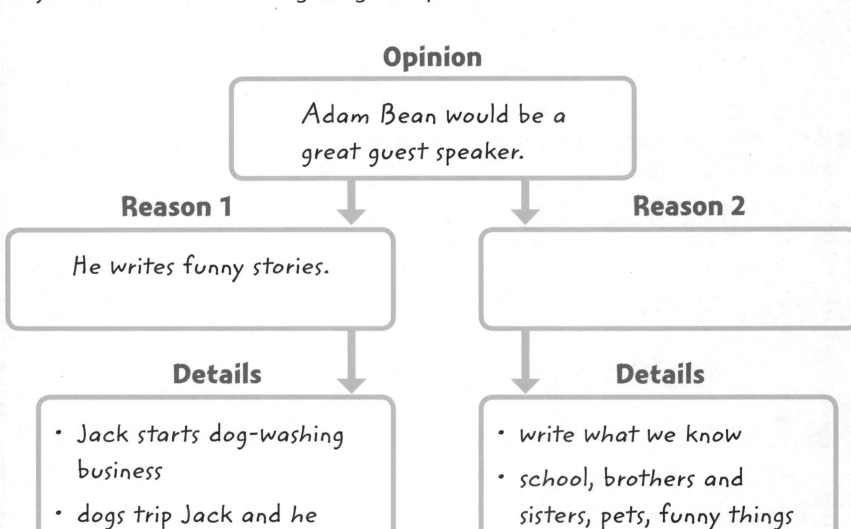

Opinion

Adam Bean would be a great guest speaker.

Reason 1

He writes funny stories.

Reason 2

Details

- Jack starts dog-washing business
- dogs trip Jack and he falls into the tub
- Jack gets bath instead

Details

- write what we know
- school, brothers and sisters, pets, funny things
- makes us better writers

1 **Fill in** the second reason Danna included in her letter.

Use the chart below to plan your writing.

2 **Fill in** your opinion and your reasons.

3 **Write** details that support each of your reasons.

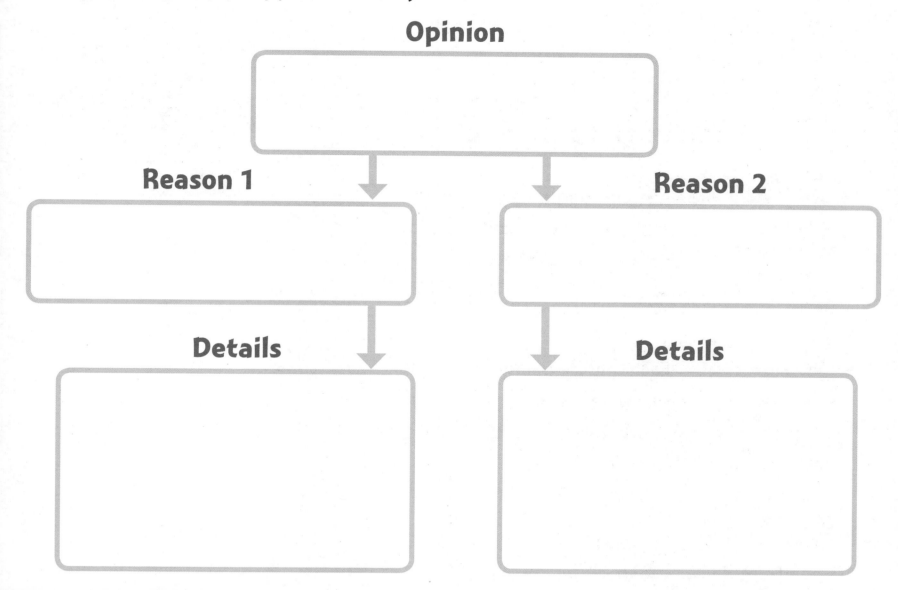

Opinion

Reason 1

Reason 2

Details

Details

Independent Practice

Write Time Write a sentence that tells what action you want your reader to take.

W.2.1: Write opinion pieces in which they introduce the topic or book, state an opinion. . . .

Step 5 Draft

This chart shows the parts of an opinion letter. Use the ideas here as you draft your beginning, middle, and end.

Parts of an Opinion Letter

BEGINNING	A strong **beginning** should:
States your opinion about the topic	• Give your **purpose** for writing. • State your **opinion.**

MIDDLE	Each **middle** paragraph should:
Gives reasons to support your opinion	• Give a **reason** for your opinion. • Give **details** to support the reason.

END	The **end** of your letter should:
Asks the reader to take action	• **Restate** your opinion. • Ask your reader to **take action.**

Write the BEGINNING

Study the beginning of Danna's letter. Then try writing the beginning of your letter.

BEGINNING

MIDDLE

END

MENTOR TEXT

> April 23, 2015
>
> Dear Mrs. Wadi,
>
> I am writing to say that Adam Bean should be our guest speaker for Author Day. Adam Bean is my favorite author. I think he would be a great guest speaker. I hope you will agree.

1 **Underline** Danna's purpose for writing.

MY LETTER

2 **Write** the first sentence of your letter.

_____

_____

HINT What is your purpose for writing?

Independent Practice

 Write Time Draft the beginning of your letter. Use the tips from the chart on page 168.

Turn and Talk What should your beginning include?

W.2.1: Write opinion pieces in which they . . . supply reasons that support the opinion . . . and provide a concluding statement or section.

Write the MIDDLE

Read one reason that Danna gives in her letter. Then try writing one of your reasons.

MENTOR TEXT

> Adam Bean writes funny stories. In *Dog Gone*, Jack starts a dog-washing business. But he doesn't know that dogs hate baths! The nervous dogs race around wildly trying to escape, and Jack falls into the tub. The only one who gets a bath is Jack!

1 **Underline** the reason Danna gives.

2 **Draw a box** around the details that support her reason.

MY LETTER

3 **Write** a sentence that tells one of your reasons. Add a sentence with details that support the reason.

> **HINT** Review your reasons and details on page 167.

_____

_____

Write the END

Study the end of Danna's letter. Then try writing the end of your letter.

BEGINNING

↓

MIDDLE

↓

END

MENTOR TEXT

> Adam Bean would be the best guest speaker. He writes funny stories and could help us to be better writers. Please invite Adam Bean to be our guest speaker on Author Day. You will not be sorry.

1 **Underline** the action Danna asks her reader to take.

MY LETTER

2 **Write** a sentence asking your school librarian to take action.

HINT Why are you writing this letter?

_____

_____

Independent Practice

 Write Time Finish drafting the middle and end of your letter.

Turn and Talk
How does your letter convince your reader?

W.2.5: With guidance and support from adults and peers, focus on a topic and strengthen writing as needed by revising . . .

Step 6 Revise

FOCUS Reasons and Details

 Modeled Instruction

Let's read part of Danna's draft and part of her checklist.

> Adam Bean writes funny stories. *Dog Gone* is one of those stories. I laughed at every single page! It's one of the funniest stories I have ever read.
>
> Adam Bean also gives kids like us great tips on how to write stories. He says to write what we know.

Opinion Writing Checklist

✔ Did I give reasons for my opinion?

✔ Did I include details to support my reasons?

1 **Underline** Danna's reasons.

2 How can Danna improve her draft?

_____

_____

_____

I wrote about the story I liked more. Can you help me make this part of my draft better?

> Kids will enjoy the story because it could happen to any of us. It was a really good story and I think second graders will really like reading it.

3 **Underline** Hershel's reason.

4 **Revise** Hershel's details to better support his reason.

_____

_____

_____

HINT Each supporting detail should tell more about the reason.

Independent Practice

 Write Time Use the Opinion Writing Checklist to help you revise your writing.

Turn and Talk How do reasons and supporting details work together?

Lesson 6 **Step 6 Revise** continued

L.2.6: Use words and phrases acquired through conversations, reading and being read to, and responding to texts, including using adjectives and adverbs to describe.

FOCUS Descriptive Words

 Modeled Instruction

Descriptive words give details that help readers understand something better or make a picture in their minds. Read the following examples.

Plain Words	Descriptive Words
The popsicle dripped syrup down my hand.	The **icy** popsicle dripped **bright red** syrup down my hand.
The song made the kids laugh.	The **silly** song made the kids **giggle**.

Let's see how Danna used descriptive words in her letter.

 **MENTOR TEXT**

Adam Bean writes funny stories. In *Dog Gone*, Jack starts a dog-washing business. But he doesn't know that dogs hate baths! The nervous dogs race around wildly trying to escape, and Jack falls into the tub. The only one who gets a bath is Jack!

Think Aloud

- The word *funny* describes the kind of stories the author writes. It tells my principal why I like this author.

- The words *nervous* and *wildly* show how the dogs were behaving. They help my principal picture what makes the story funny.

Revise each sentence that Hershel wrote in his letter. Choose descriptive words from the word bank.

frustrated	gigantic	clever
loudly	sadly	excitedly

1 The author puts words and pictures together in a

_____ way to tell the story.

> **HINT** Which word tells how the author writes?

2 The _____ boy _____

realizes his parents won't come because he lied.

> **HINT** Which words tell how the boy feels?

3 Many of us would want our parents to see a

_____ parade balloon.

Independent Practice

 Write Time Try adding some descriptive words to your letter.

Turn and Talk
How can descriptive words make your opinion writing more convincing?

Step 7 Edit

W.2.5: With guidance and support from adults and peers, focus on a topic and strengthen writing as needed by . . . editing.

L.2.2b: Use commas in greetings and closings of letters.

FOCUS Commas

Modeled Instruction

Commas are punctuation marks that separate information and show where to pause. They help to make writing clearer.

Commas in Letters	
Between the Day and Year	May 15, 2015
After the Greeting	Dear Mr. Romo,
After the Closing	Sincerely, Indra

Language Handbook To learn more about commas, turn to page 210.

Read part of Danna's draft below.

MENTOR TEXT Draft

April 23 2015

Dear Mrs. Wadi,

    I am writing to say that Adam Bean should be our guest speaker for Author Day.

1 **Circle** the comma that Danna used in her letter.

2 **Add** the comma that Danna is missing.

Guided Practice

Add commas in the correct places.

3 March 11 2015

HINT Separate the month and day from the year.

4 Dear Mr. Carter

5 Truly yours

6 Dear Mom

HINT Show a pause after your greeting.

7 July 4 1776

Independent Practice

Write Time Check that you used commas correctly. Check your spelling, capitalization, and other punctuation marks, also.

Turn and Talk
How can commas make your letter easier to read?

W.2.6: With guidance and support from adults . . . produce and publish writing, including in collaboration with peers.

Step 8 Publish and Share

FOCUS Describe Key Ideas

 **Prepare**

Talk to others who wrote about the same story as you.
Ask: Why did you choose this story? Then **take notes** on their reasons.

My Story _____

Share

Talk to classmates who chose the other story. **Take notes** on their reasons for choosing that story.

The Other Story _____

Independent Practice

Write Your Opinion Letter

Which story would second graders enjoy reading?

Language Handbook

Table of Contents

Language Handbook *continued*

Lesson 1
Nouns

L.2.1: Demonstrate command of the conventions of standard English grammar and usage when writing or speaking.

Introduction A **noun** is a word that names a person, place, or thing.

- A **common noun** names any person, place, or thing.
- A **proper noun** names a certain person, place, or thing. It begins with a capital letter.

	Common Nouns	**Proper Nouns**
Person	boy, aunt	Daniel, Aunt Maria
Place	street, store	King Street, Super Toy Shop
Thing	dog, game	Sparky, Crazy Cards

Guided Practice Underline the noun or nouns in each sentence. Then write each noun in the chart to tell what it names.

HINT A proper noun can be more than one word. Each important word in a proper noun begins with a capital letter.

1. Uncle Marco needs a new hat.

2. We take the bus to the Top Shop.

3. A woman sells us a green Cappy Cap.

4. We leave the store and walk to the park.

Person	**Place**	**Thing**

Independent Practice

Choose the correct word or words to answer each question.

1 Which words in this sentence are **nouns**?

My friends went to the mall.

A friends, went

B My, friends

C friends, mall

D went, mall

2 Which noun in this sentence names a **person**?

Lilly got a new shirt for school.

A Lilly

B new

C shirt

D school

3 Which noun in this sentence names a **place**?

Raj got a big pretzel at the Snacky Shack.

A Raj

B big

C pretzel

D Snacky Shack

4 Which noun in this sentence names a **thing**?

Cleo got a gift for her friend Pablo.

A Cleo

B gift

C friend

D Pablo

Lesson 2
Plural Nouns

L.2.1b: Form and use frequently occurring irregular plural nouns (e.g., *feet, children, teeth, mice, fish*).

👥 Introduction
A **singular noun** is a noun that names one person, place, or thing. A **plural noun** names more than one person, place, or thing.

- You can form the plural of most nouns by adding **-s** or **-es**.

Singular	bird	glass	bush	fox
Plural	bird**s**	glass**es**	bush**es**	fox**es**

- Some plurals change in special ways or do not change at all. You just have to remember them.

Change in Special Ways					
Singular	child	foot	tooth	mouse	goose	man
Plural	children	feet	teeth	mice	geese	men

Do Not Change			
Singular	deer	fish	moose	sheep
Plural	deer	fish	moose	sheep

👥 Guided Practice
Write the plural of the noun to complete each sentence.

HINT If a noun ends in **tch**, add **-es** to make it plural.

Example:
ditch + es =
ditches

1 Two _____ walk in the woods.
child

2 They hop over some _____ of mud.
patch

3 Do you see those _____ in the dirt?
track

4 This animal has four _____.
foot

👤 Independent Practice

Choose the correct plural of the noun to complete each sentence.

1 The pond is full of many _____.

   A fish

   B fishs

   C fishes

   D feesh

2 Six _____ swim on the water.

   A gooses

   B geeses

   C geese

   D goose

3 Three _____ live near the pond.

   A mices

   B mouse

   C mouses

   D mice

Read the sentence. Circle the plural noun that is spelled incorrectly. Then write the word correctly.

4 Three childs saw five moose through the trees and bushes.

   _____

Lesson 3
Collective Nouns

L.2.1a: Use collective nouns (e.g., *group*).

 **Introduction** A **noun** names a person, place, or thing. Some nouns name groups of people, animals, or other things that go together.

a **crowd** of people

a **pile** of leaves

a **herd** of buffalo

a **school** of fish

a **pack** of wolves

a **swarm** of bees

a **bunch** of bananas

a **flock** of birds

Guided Practice Circle the noun that names a group in each sentence.

HINT A noun that names a group often comes before the word *of.*

1 A herd of cows stood in the field.

2 The horse ate a bunch of carrots.

3 The dog chased a flock of geese.

4 The chickens pecked at a pile of seeds.

5 A swarm of flies buzzed around the pigs.

6 A crowd of children watched the sheep.

Independent Practice

Choose the correct word to answer each question.

1. Which word can name a group of dogs?

   A flock

   B swarm

   C pack

   D bunch

2. Which word can name a group of sticks?

   A herd

   B school

   C swarm

   D pile

3. Which noun correctly completes this sentence?

   I see a _____ of fish swimming in the pond.

   A school

   B herd

   C pile

   D flock

Write the best word from the box to complete the sentence.

> flock
>
> bunch
>
> crowd
>
> swarm

4. The farmer picked a

   _____ of grapes.

Lesson 4
Pronouns

L.2.1: Demonstrate command of the conventions of standard English grammar and usage when writing or speaking.

Introduction A **pronoun** is a word that takes the place of a noun. Pronouns can be **singular** or **plural**.

- Some pronouns take the place of a noun that tells who or what does something.

He ~~Sam~~ plays. They ~~Sam's friends~~ sing. It ~~The music~~ sounds great.

Singular (One)					Plural (More Than One)		
I	you	he	she	it	we	you	they

- Some pronouns take the place of a noun that follows an action word. They might come after a word such as *to, for,* or *from*.

Sam plays ~~guitar~~ it. Sam plays for ~~Mr. and Mrs. Chung~~ them.

Singular (One)					Plural (More Than One)		
me	you	him	her	it	us	you	them

Guided Practice Circle the pronoun that can take the place of the underlined word or words.

HINT A plural pronoun can take the place of two or more words.

Example:
Boys and girls play music.
They play music.

1 The class learns from <u>Mr. Chung</u>.　　him　　he　　them

2 <u>Katya</u> plays the piano.　　She　　It　　Her

3 David plays <u>the tuba</u>.　　them　　it　　us

4 <u>Timor and Liz</u> play horns.　　Them　　He　　They

5 They play for <u>Maya and me</u>.　　we　　her　　us

👤 Independent Practice

Choose the pronoun that can take the place of the underlined word or words.

1 <u>Simon</u> blows the horn.

A They

B We

C Him

D He

2 Haley pounds on <u>the drum</u>.

A it

B them

C him

D me

3 <u>Maya and I</u> stomp our feet.

A You

B We

C It

D Us

4 Mr. Chung covers <u>his ears</u>!

A they

B it

C them

D her

Lesson 5
Reflexive Pronouns

L.2.1c: Use reflexive pronouns (e.g., *myself, ourselves*).

 **Introduction** A **pronoun** is a word that takes the place of a noun. A **reflexive pronoun** refers back to a noun or pronoun at the beginning of a sentence. Reflexive pronouns end in -*self* or -*selves*. They can refer back to singular or plural nouns or pronouns.

Eva drew **herself**.   We painted pictures of **ourselves**.

Singular (One)	myself, yourself, himself, herself, itself
Plural (More Than One)	ourselves, yourselves, themselves

Guided Practice Choose the reflexive pronoun that refers back to the underlined word in each sentence. Write the reflexive pronoun that correctly completes the sentence.

myself	yourself	himself	itself	themselves

HINT Reflexive pronouns usually come after action words or after words such as *by, to, of,* and *on.*

1 I drew a picture of _____.

2 Some children spilled paint on _____.

3 Leo almost cut _____ with the scissors.

👤 Independent Practice

Choose the correct pronoun to complete each sentence.

1 Nelly got _____ some clay.

  A myself

  B yourself

  C herself

  D itself

2 I covered _____ with a smock.

  A herself

  B ourselves

  C himself

  D myself

3 We made clay pots for _____.

  A himself

  B themselves

  C ourselves

  D itself

Write the correct pronoun from the box to complete the sentence.

> himself
>
> themselves
>
> yourselves

4 The boys worked quietly by

_____.

Lesson 6
Verbs

L.2.1: Demonstrate command of the conventions of standard English grammar and usage when writing or speaking.

Introduction A **verb** is a word that tells what someone or something does or is. A verb can tell what is happening now.

- An **action verb** tells what someone or something **does**.

  I **throw** the ball.

  The ball **drops** through the hoop.

- A **linking verb** tells what someone or something **is** or **is like**. The words *is, are,* and *am* are linking verbs.

  Chrissy **is** our tallest player.

  Are all basketball players tall?

  I **am** on a basketball team.

Guided Practice Circle the verb in each sentence.

HINT The linking verbs *is, are,* and *am* can be the first word of a question.

Example:

Is the game over?

1 This game is exciting.

2 Our players run down the court.

3 Chrissy catches the ball.

4 She jumps high.

5 The ball bounces on the rim.

6 Are we the winners?

Independent Practice

Choose the word that answers each question.

1 Which word in this sentence is a **verb**?

Jacob and Chrissy are the best players.

A   Jacob

B   are

C   best

D   players

2 Which word in this sentence is a **verb**?

Our team wins every basketball game.

A   team

B   wins

C   every

D   game

3 Which of these words is an **action verb**?

The crowd cheers when the game is over.

A   cheers

B   game

C   is

D   over

4 Which word in this sentence is a **linking verb**?

I am so happy!

A   happy

B   I

C   am

D   so

Lesson 7
Past Tense of Irregular Verbs

L.2.1d: Form and use the past tense of frequently occurring irregular verbs (e.g., *sat, hid, told*).

Introduction A **verb** tells what someone or something does or is. A **past-tense verb** shows an action that happened in the past.

- The letters -*ed* at the end of a verb show an action that happened in the past.

  Today, I **walk** to the pool. Yesterday, I **walked** to the pool.

- Some verbs are **irregular**. They change in special ways to show an action that happened in the past. You just have to remember these.

  Today, I **go** to the pool. Yesterday, I **went** to the pool.

Now	sit	come	get	see	tell	run
In the Past	sat	came	got	saw	told	ran

Guided Practice Circle the correct past-tense verb to complete each sentence.

HINT Use the chart to find the correct spelling of each irregular past-tense verb.

1 Last week, I _____ Aldo at the pool.   sees   saw

2 We _____ by the side of the pool.   sat   sits

3 Then we _____ into the water.   jumps   jumped

4 Aldo _____ me he was cold.   told   telled

5 We _____ out of the cold water.   getted   got

Independent Practice

Choose the correct past-tense verb.

1 Yesterday, Shia _____ to the beach.

   A go

   B goes

   C went

   D goed

2 Tommy _____ to the beach with me last week.

   A came

   B come

   C comed

   D camed

3 The life guard _____ in a tall chair.

   A sit

   B sited

   C sate

   D sat

4 Mom _____ me to be careful in the water.

   A told

   B toll

   C tell

   D teld

Lesson 8
Adjectives and Adverbs

L.2.1e: Use adjectives and adverbs, and choose between them depending on what is to be modified.

 **Introduction** An **adjective** is a word that tells more about a noun. Adjectives usually tell "what kind" or "how many."

My jacket is **green**.   It has **two** pockets.

What Kind	red, loud, old, sweet, happy
How Many	one, ten, few, some, many

An **adverb** is a word that tells more about a verb.

- Adverbs often tell "how." These adverbs usually end in *-ly*.

I **quickly** zip my jacket.   I tie my shoes **tightly**.

- Adverbs can also tell "when" or "where."

I **soon** leave.   I run **outside**.

How	slowly, loudly, lightly, carefully
When	later, next, soon, yesterday
Where	there, nearby, somewhere

Guided Practice Write "adjective" or "adverb" to name each underlined word. Then circle the noun or verb that it tells about.

HINT Adjectives and adverbs do not always go beside the word they tell about.

1 Tia has lost her <u>purple</u> scarf. _____

2 She wore it to school <u>yesterday</u>. _____

3 <u>Two</u> friends look for it. _____

4 They look <u>everywhere</u>. _____

👤 Independent Practice

Choose the word that answers each question.

1 Which word in this sentence is an **adjective**?

The friends quickly find the purple scarf.

A purple

B scarf

C find

D quickly

2 Which word in this sentence is an **adverb**?

Tia thanks her good friends gladly.

A good

B thanks

C friends

D gladly

Write the correct word from the box to complete each sentence.

widely	three

3 My jeans have _____ holes in them.

today	warm

4 Bring a scarf with you _____ .

Lesson 9
Complete Sentences

L.2.1: Demonstrate command of the conventions of standard English grammar and usage when writing or speaking.

Introduction A **sentence** is a group of words that tells a complete thought.

- Every sentence has a **subject**. The subject names the person or thing that the sentence is about.

  subject
  The children play in the park.

- Every sentence has a **predicate**. The predicate tells what the subject does or is.

  predicate
  They **love the big playground**.

- A sentence begins with a **capital letter**. It ends with a **period**.

Guided Practice Read each sentence. Above the underlined words, write "S" for "Subject" or "P" for "Predicate."

HINT The subject can name more than one person or thing.

1 The kids run on the playground.

2 Gracie goes down the slide.

3 Two children swing from the bars.

4 Mom and Uncle Ray sit on a bench.

5 A black dog runs across the playground.

Independent Practice

Choose the correct group of words to answer each question.

1 What is the **subject** of this sentence?

Two teams play kickball.

A   play kickball

B   teams play

C   Two teams

D   kickball

2 What is the **predicate** of this sentence?

Kevin and Maria chase the ball.

A   chase the ball

B   Kevin and Maria chase

C   Kevin and Maria

D   the ball

3 Which of these is a complete sentence?

A   The red ball.

B   Rolls into a puddle.

C   Right into a big puddle.

D   The ball rolls into a puddle.

4 Which of these is a complete sentence?

A   The cute little dog.

B   The dog stands by the ball.

C   The little dog and the red ball.

D   Stands by the red ball.

Lesson 10
Simple and Compound Sentences

L.2.1f: Produce, expand, and rearrange complete simple and compound sentences (e.g., *The boy watched the movie; The little boy watched the movie; The action movie was watched by the little boy*).

Introduction A **sentence** is a group of words that tells a complete thought.

- A **simple sentence** has <u>one subject</u> and <u>one predicate</u>.

    subject   predicate
    Many people love pets.

- A **compound sentence** is <u>two simple sentences</u> joined together by a word such as *or, and,* or *but*.

    simple sentence   simple sentence
    Luis likes dogs, **but** Helen likes cats.

Guided Practice   Write a joining word to complete each compound sentence.

| and | but | or |

HINT Place a comma before the joining word.

1 Helen feeds her cat Leo _____ she plays with him.

2 Leo likes chicken _____ he likes fish better.

3 Leo naps on a chair _____ he sleeps in his bed.

4 Helen's sister wants a snake _____ Dad does not like snakes.

5 He likes turtles _____ he loves frogs.

6 Leo might like a frog _____ he might scare it.

👤 Independent Practice

Choose the correct way to join the two simple sentences.

1 Anna got a frog. She put it in a tank.

A Anna got a frog and, she put it in a tank.

B Anna got a frog, and, she put it in a tank.

C Anna got a frog, she put it in a tank.

D Anna got a frog, and she put it in a tank.

2 The frog eats many things. It does not like vegetables.

A The frog eats many things, but, it does not like vegetables.

B The frog eats many things, but it does not like vegetables.

C The frog eats many things, it does not like vegetables.

D The frog eats many things but, it does not like vegetables.

3 Leo will watch the frog quietly. He will meow at it.

A Leo will watch the frog quietly or, he will meow at it.

B Leo will watch the frog, quietly or he will meow at it.

C Leo will watch the frog quietly, or he will meow at it.

D Leo will watch the frog quietly, he will meow at it.

Underline the two simple sentences in the compound sentence. Circle the joining word.

4 Helen picks up Leo, and she takes him away.

Lesson 11

Capitalization in Holidays, Product Names, and Geographic Names

L.2.2a: Capitalize holidays, product names, and geographic names.

Introduction
The names of **holidays, products,** and **places** like towns, states, and countries are proper nouns. Use capital letters correctly when you write them.

- Begin each word of a holiday, product, or place with a capital letter.
- Do not begin words such as *for* and *of* with a capital letter.

Holidays	Thanksgiving, Presidents' Day, Fourth of July
Products	Speedy Sneakers, Kites for Kids, Tummy Yums
Places	Hilltown, North Carolina, United States of America

Guided Practice
Read each sentence. Write the name of each underlined holiday, product, or place correctly.

HINT The word *day* is part of the name of many holidays. Remember to begin it with a capital letter.

1 The <u>fourth of july</u> is a fun holiday.

_____

2 People in the <u>united states of america</u> celebrate every year.

_____

3 Some cities, such as <u>boston</u>, have fireworks.

_____

4 My family eats treats called <u>freezy pops</u>.

_____

5 This holiday is also called <u>independence day</u>.

_____

Independent Practice

Choose the correct way to write the underlined words in each sentence.

Read the sentence. Circle the three words that should begin with a capital letter.

1 Two other American holidays are Thanksgiving and <u>flag day</u>.

   A   flag day

   B   flag Day

   C   Flag day

   D   Flag Day

4 I like to stay up late on new year's eve.

2 The city of <u>new orleans</u> has parades on some holidays.

   A   New orleans

   B   new Orleans

   C   New Orleans

   D   new orleans

3 Kids blow loud horns called <u>happy honkers</u>.

   A   Happy honkers

   B   Happy Honkers

   C   happy Honkers

   D   happy honkers

Lesson 12

L.2.2b: Use commas in greetings and closings of letters.

Punctuating Greetings and Closings of Letters

Introduction
When you write a letter to someone, you begin with a **greeting**. You end with a **closing**.

greeting ——▶ Dear Nana**,**

Thank you for the scooter. It is my favorite gift!

closing ——▶ Yours truly**,**

Trina

• Use a **comma** (**,**) after the greeting and closing of a letter.

Guided Practice
Add commas where they belong in the first two letters. Then write a closing for the third letter.

HINT When you write a greeting or closing, you begin the first word with a capital letter.

1 Dear Bin

I got a red bike for my birthday! Can you come visit?

Your friend

Harold

2 Dear Harold

I hope to visit soon. I want to ride your new bike!

Best wishes

Bin

3 Dear Tracy,

I got a letter from Bin. He may visit soon!

_____

Harold

👤 Independent Practice

Read each question. Then choose the correct answer.

1 How should this **greeting** be written?

Dear Mr. Gomez

A Dear Mr. Gomez?

B Dear, Mr. Gomez,

C Dear, Mr. Gomez

D Dear Mr. Gomez,

2 How should this **closing** be written?

Very truly yours

A Very truly yours,

B Very truly yours!

C Very truly yours.

D Very truly yours

Read the letter. Then rewrite the greeting and closing correctly.

Dear, Papa

Thank you for the book. I can't wait to find out how it ends.

Lots of love.
Rachel

3 _____

4 _____

Lesson 13
Contractions

L.2.2c: Use an apostrophe to form contractions . . .

Introduction A **contraction** is a short way of putting two words together.

- When you write a contraction, you leave one or more letters out.

  I + am = **I'm**   I'm strong and healthy.

- An **apostrophe** (') takes the place of the missing letters.

she + **is** = she's	**do** + **not** = don't
we + **will** = we'll	**does** + **not** = doesn't
is + **not** = isn't	**did** + **not** = didn't
cannot = can't	**are** + **not** = aren't

Guided Practice Read each sentence. Write a contraction for the underlined word or words.

HINT To form most contractions, drop only the vowel of the second word. But for *cannot* and contractions with *will,* drop the consonant before the vowel, too.

can**no**t = can't

we **wi**ll = we'll

1 I am making muffins with my sister. _____

2 She is a good baker. _____

3 We will use butter and eggs. _____

4 We cannot forget the flour! _____

5 I do not want nuts in the muffins. _____

6 My brother does not like nuts either. _____

Independent Practice

Read each question. Choose the correct answer.

1 Which contraction for "did not" is written correctly?

A didnt'

B di'dnt

C didn't

D did'not

2 Which contraction for "we will" is written correctly?

A we'll

B we'ill

C well'

D we'l

3 Which contraction for "she is" is written correctly?

A she'is

B she's

C shes'

D shes

Read the sentence. Circle the contraction that is not written correctly.

4 Dad can't find the box of raisins. It is'nt on the shelf.

Lesson 14
Possessive Nouns

L.2.2c: Use an apostrophe to form . . . frequently occurring possessives.

Introduction A **possessive noun** names a person or thing that something belongs to.

> **a tail** belonging to a whale = **a** whale's **tail**

A possessive noun has an **apostrophe (').**

- If a noun is <u>singular</u>, add an apostrophe and **-s** to the end of the word.

> **whale + 's = A** whale's **tail is very strong.**

- If a noun is <u>plural</u> and already ends with **-s**, just add the apostrophe after the **-s**.

> **whales + ' = Look at those** whales' **tails!**

Guided Practice Add an apostrophe and -s or just an apostrophe to make the correct possessive noun in each sentence.

HINT A plural noun names more than one person, place, or thing, and usually ends with -s.

1 A whale_____ baby is called a calf.

2 The two babies_____ faces are very cute.

3 The three scientists_____ job is to study whales.

4 Special fat keeps these animals_____ bodies warm.

5 A whale does not have teeth like a shark_____ teeth.

Independent Practice

Choose the correct way to write each underlined noun.

1 <u>Lindas</u> teacher told the class about whales.

   A   Lindas'

   B   Linda's

   C   Lindas's

   D   Linda's'

2 The <u>teachers</u> photos of whales were amazing.

   A   teachers's

   B   teache'rs

   C   teachers

   D   teacher's

3 Many <u>students</u> reports had drawings of whales.

   A   students'

   B   students's

   C   student's

   D   students

Write the correct word from the box to complete the sentence.

Jason's'
Jason's
Jasons's
Jasons

4 _____ mother studies sharks.

Lesson 15
Spelling Patterns

L.2.2d: Generalize learned spelling patterns when writing words (e.g., cage ⟶ badge; boy ⟶ boil).

Introduction Some vowel sounds can be spelled more than one way.

- The vowel sound you hear in *boy* can be spelled **oy** or **oi**. Use **oy** if the sound is at the end of the word. Use **oi** if it is in the middle.

| boy | joy | toy | boil | noise | coin |

- The vowel sound you hear in *day* can be spelled **ay** or **ai**. Use **ay** if the sound is at the end of the word. Use **ai** if it is in the middle.

| day | play | spray | train | wait | paint |

Guided Practice Circle the correct letter pair that completes each word. Then write it on the line.

HINT Use **ai** or **oi** if the vowel sound is at the beginning of the word.

Examples:

aid   **oi**nk

1 The b_____ rides a red scooter.   **oy**   **oi**

2 The wheels make a strange n_____se.   **oy**   **oi**

3 He uses _____l to stop the squeak.   **oy**   **oi**

4 He may p_____nt his scooter blue.   **ay**   **ai**

5 Maybe he can spr_____ it on.   **ay**   **ai**

Independent Practice

Choose the correct way to spell the missing word in each sentence.

1 The sky is stormy and very _____ .

A gray

B grai

C graiy

D gra

2 The bad weather may _____ the hike.

A spoyl

B spoil

C spail

D spoyil

Write the correct spelling of the underlined word in each sentence.

3 The <u>rayn</u> comes down hard.

_____

4 I do not <u>enjoi</u> this weather.

_____

Lesson 16
Using a Dictionary to Check Spelling

L.2.2e: Consult reference materials, including beginning dictionaries, as needed to check and correct spellings.

 **Introduction** A **dictionary** lists words and their meanings. The words are shown in **alphabetical order**, or from **A** to **Z**. The **guide words** at the top of each page tell the first and last word on the page.

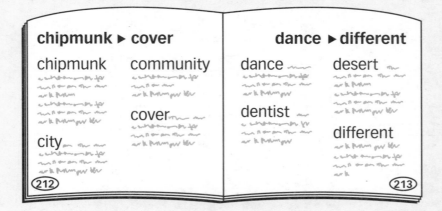

You can use a dictionary to check a word's spelling. First, find a page that shows words with the same **first letter** as your word. Use the guide words to help you. Next, look at the **second letter** of each word to see if yours comes before or after it.

 **Guided Practice** Check the spelling of each underlined word. Write the correct spelling on the line.

HINT Look at the guide words on each page . If your word comes between them in the alphabet, it is on that page.

1 A <u>comunity</u> is where you live. _____

2 Many people live and work in a <u>citty</u>. _____

3 Workers do <u>differrint</u> jobs. _____

4 A <u>dentest</u> takes care of teeth. _____

Independent Practice

Use a dictionary to check the spelling of each underlined word. Then choose the correct spelling.

1 Some workers wear special <u>clohse</u> and hats.

   A clohs

   B clothes

   C cloths

   D clohz

2 The police keep people out of <u>danjer</u>.

   A danger

   B dainger

   C danjer

   D dangor

3 Firefighters must often <u>crall</u> through smoke.

   A crawll

   B crawle

   C crall

   D crawl

4 A <u>doctor</u> treats people who are sick or hurt.

   A doctur

   B docktor

   C docter

   D doctor

Lesson 17

L.2.3a: Compare formal and informal uses of English.

Comparing Formal and Informal Uses of English

Introduction The words we use when we speak or write depend on whom we are speaking or writing to.

- We use "everyday" English with our friends and family. For example, we use short words and phrases called **slang** and **contractions**.

> Hi! What's up?
> I'm going to a movie. Can't wait!

- We use **formal** English with people we do not know well, or when we are in school. We use complete sentences and avoid slang and contractions.

> Hello, Mr. Chang. How are you?
> I am looking forward to the movie about pandas.

Everyday English	Formal English
yeah	yes
can't	cannot
Thanks a lot!	Thank you very much!
Sorry about that.	I apologize for my mistake.
All done!	I am finished.

Guided Practice Read each example of everyday English. Next to it, write the letter of the formal way to say it.

HINT *Don't* is a contraction of "Do not." *That's* is a contraction of "That is."

1. I don't get it. _____
2. Best book ever! _____
3. How's it going? _____
4. Yup, that's right. _____

a Yes, that is correct.

b How are you today?

c I do not understand.

d I liked this book very much.

Independent Practice

Choose the answer to each question.

1 What is the best way to greet an important person at your school?

   A Hey.

   B What's up, dude?

   C Hi there!

   D Hello.

2 Read this sentence from a book report. What is the best way to rewrite it?

   I can't believe the ending was so weird.

   A I didn't like the ending. Not a bit.

   B I found the ending difficult to believe.

   C Boo, what a boring ending!

   D I totally didn't get the ending.

3 Which word or words make the underlined word in this sentence more formal?

   This book is about why penguins <u>don't</u> fly.

   A wanna

   B are not gonna

   C do not

   D can't even

Rewrite the underlined words to be more formal.

4 Dear Captain Rodriguez,

   I enjoyed your talk. <u>Thanks a bunch</u> for coming to our class.

   _____

   _____

Lesson 18

L.2.4a: Use sentence-level context as a clue to the meaning of a word or phrase.

Using Context Clues

Introduction When you see a word you don't know, look at the other words in the sentence. They can give you **clues** about what the word means.

- Sometimes other words in a sentence tell the **definition**, or meaning, of the word.

  definition
  The tops of trees in rain forests form a canopy, or **covering of leaves**.

- Sometimes other words in a sentence give an **example** that helps explain what the word means.

  example
  The forest canopy is like a **really big sun hat**.

Guided Practice Look at the underlined word in each sentence. Circle the other words that help you understand what the word means.

HINT Look for the words *or, like,* and *such as*. They often come before clues that help you figure out what a word means.

1 Many creatures, or animals, live in the rain forest.

2 Big flocks, or groups, of birds dive through the sky.

3 Mammals, like tigers and monkeys, climb on high branches.

4 Bright blue butterflies flutter, or fly, between tall trees.

5 Tiny amphibians such as frogs hide in the leaves.

6 Enormous snakes can be 30 feet long.

Independent Practice

Read the sentence below. Then answer the questions.

Big and small <u>nocturnal</u> animals only come out at night.

1 What do <u>nocturnal</u> animals do?

    A stay asleep all the time

    B come out when it gets dark

    C stay inside all the time

    D come out only during the day

2 Which words help you know what <u>nocturnal</u> means?

    A animals only

    B Big and small

    C only come out at night

    D animals come

Read the sentence below. Then answer the questions.

Wild cats hunt for <u>prey</u>, or food, after dark.

3 What does the word "prey" mean?

    A where wild cats live

    B when wild cats sleep

    C what wild cats look like

    D what wild cats eat

4 Which word helps you know what the word "prey" means?

    A cats

    B food

    C dark

    D wild

Lesson 19
Prefixes

L.2.4b: Determine the meaning of the new word formed when a known prefix is added to a known word (e.g., *happy/unhappy, tell/retell*).

Introduction You can use word parts to figure out what a word means.

A **prefix** is a word part added to the beginning of a word. It changes the meaning of the word.

Prefix	Meaning	Prefix + Word	New Word	Meaning
un-	**"not"**	un + **fair**	un**fair**	**not fair**
re-	**"again"**	re + **tell**	re**tell**	**tell again**
pre-	**"before"**	pre + **pay**	pre**pay**	**pay before**

Guided Practice Look at the prefix in each underlined word. Then circle the correct meaning of the word.

HINT When you see a long word with a prefix, first look for a word you know in it. Then cover that word with your finger and look at the prefix. Think about what the prefix means and add the meaning to the word you know.

1 Dad and I are <u>unhappy</u> with our tree fort.

happy again   not happy

2 We will <u>rebuild</u> it.

build again   not build

3 The roof is broken and <u>unsafe</u>.

not safe   safe again

4 This time we will <u>preplan</u> how to build it.

not plan   plan before

5 We buy <u>precut</u> boards for the walls and roof.

cut before   not cut

Independent Practice

Look at the prefix in each underlined word. Then choose the correct meaning of the word.

1 We <u>redo</u> the walls of our fort.

   A do again

   B not do

   C do before

   D do wrong

2 We save the <u>unbroken</u> boards.

   A broken again

   B broken before

   C very broken

   D not broken

3 We <u>pretest</u> the old boards to be sure they are strong.

   A test again and again

   B do not test

   C test before

   D test later

4 We <u>repaint</u> the whole fort.

   A not paint

   B paint again

   C paint quickly

   D paint before

Lesson 20
Root Words

L.2.4c: Use a known root word as a clue to the meaning of an unknown word with the same root (e.g., *addition, additional*).

 **Introduction** Some words can be broken into parts. The main part of the word is called a **root word**. The root word will help you figure out the meaning of the whole word.

For example, to help means to make it easier for someone to do something.

help	Ann will help us learn about weather.
helper	She is a great helper.
helpful	She is a very helpful person.
helping	She is helping us learn about clouds.

Guided Practice **Circle the root word in each underlined word. Then draw a line from the sentence to the meaning of the word.**

HINT If a word has an ending such as *-er* or *-y*, cover the ending with your finger, and read the smaller word. Think about what that word means.

1 Weather <u>watchers</u> study clouds.

people who look at something

2 Clouds give <u>useful</u> hints about weather.

getting dark

3 <u>Puffy</u> clouds mean the day will be nice.

helpful

4 <u>Darkening</u> clouds mean it might rain.

soft and light

Independent Practice

Look for the root word in each underlined word. Use this smaller word to help you answer the questions.

1 Read the sentence below.

> Be <u>careful</u> when you see big, dark clouds.

What does the word "careful" mean in the sentence?

A quiet

B safe

C noisy

D silly

2 Read the sentence below.

> <u>Dangerous</u> weather may be coming.

What does the word "Dangerous" mean in the sentence?

A good

B sunny

C cold

D harmful

3 Read the sentence below.

> Bad weather can move <u>quickly</u>.

What does the word "quickly" mean in the sentence?

A fast

B soon

C slowly

D loudly

4 Read the sentence below.

> Don't get caught in <u>stormy</u> weather!

What does the word "stormy" mean in the sentence?

A having lots of sunshine

B without clouds or rain

C with a lot of wind and rain

D with clear, blue skies

Lesson 21
Compound Words

L.2.4d: Use knowledge of the meaning of individual words to predict the meaning of compound words (e.g., *birdhouse, lighthouse, housefly; bookshelf, notebook, bookmark*).

👥 **Introduction** A word that is made up of two smaller words is called a **compound** word.

Often you can figure out what a compound word means by thinking about the meanings of the two smaller words.

house   +   fly   = housefly

A housefly is a fly that gets into your house.

👥 **Guided Practice** **Put the two words together to make a compound word. Write the new word on the line. Then circle the correct meaning.**

HINT Sometimes the second word in the compound word is a big clue to the word's meaning. For example, a "dog**house**" is a house for a dog, not a dog that looks like a house.

1 black   +   bird   = _____
a bird with black feathers
a black feather shaped like a bird

2 sword   +   fish   = _____
a sword shaped like a fish
a fish with a jaw like a sword

3 rattle   +   snake   = _____
a rattle shaped like a snake
a snake with a tail like a rattle

Independent Practice

Read the compound word in each sentence. Then choose the correct meaning for the word.

1 A <u>catfish</u> uses its whiskers to find food in the sea.

  A a fish that eats bugs

  B a cat that looks like a bird

  C a fish with whiskers like a cat

  D a cat that likes boats

2 A <u>sheepdog</u> helps keep farm animals safe.

  A a sheep used for its wool

  B a dog that takes care of sheep

  C a sheep that plays with birds

  D a dog that looks like a goat

3 A <u>seahorse</u> has fins and swims in the ocean.

  A a big ocean shaped like a horse

  B a sea animal that looks like a snake

  C a horse that lives in a barn

  D a sea animal whose head looks like a horse

Choose one word from the box to complete the second sentence. Write the correct word on the line.

> earthquake   earthworm   wormhole

4 The worm digs deep into the soil. This _____ crawls up out of the ground when it rains.

Lesson 22
Using a Dictionary

L.2.4e: Use glossaries and beginning dictionaries, both print and digital, to determine or clarify the meaning of words and phrases.

Introduction A **dictionary** tells a word's **definition**, or what the word means. Some words have more than one meaning.

- How do you find the correct meaning of a word? Read each meaning to figure out which definition makes sense.
- Some dictionaries have sentences to help you understand the words.

(what the word means)   (the word used in a sentence)

block

1. a piece of wood or hard plastic used as a toy
My little sister lost the red block she was playing with.

2. an area of a city with streets on four sides
My best friend and I live in the same block.

Guided Practice Use the dictionary page above to find the correct meaning of each underlined word. Write the meaning on the line.

HINT Reread the sentence using the definition you chose. Does the sentence make sense?

1 Our class used <u>blocks</u> to make a model of our school.

_____

2 We walked around the <u>block</u> to look at the building.

_____

3 Our school takes up a whole city <u>block</u>!

_____

4 We used every <u>block</u> we had to build our model.

_____

👤 Independent Practice

Use the dictionary below to answer each question. Write the meaning that makes sense in the sentence.

story **1.** a group of words that tells about something real that happened *The story is about the first school in our city.* **2.** a floor or level in a building *The Empire State Building has 103 stories.*	**yard** **1.** an outside area near a house or building *Let's play in my yard after school.* **2.** an amount that tells how long something is *This short piece of rope is one yard long.*

1 What does the word "story" mean in this sentence?

Our teacher read a <u>story</u> about how our school was built.

_____

_____

2 What does the word "story" mean in this sentence?

The school used to be only one <u>story</u> tall.

_____

_____

3 What does the word "yard" mean in this sentence?

Long ago, our school didn't have a <u>yard</u> around it.

_____

_____

4 What does the word "yard" mean in this sentence?

Now, our big playground is almost 50 <u>yards</u> wide.

_____

_____

Lesson 23
Using a Glossary

L.2.4e: Use glossaries and beginning dictionaries, both print and digital, to determine or clarify the meaning of words and phrases.

Introduction Some books have a list of words called a **glossary**.

- A glossary is like a dictionary. It lists words in alphabetical order.
- It tells the meanings of important words in the book. Sometimes a glossary includes sentences that help you understand the word.
- You can often find the glossary near the end of a book.

> **gas** something like air that is so light it does not have a shape
> *Air is a gas we breathe.*
>
> **planet** a large ball-like object that moves around the sun
> *The Earth, where we live, is a planet.*
>
> **star** a small dot of light in the sky
> *I look for the brightest star in the sky.*

Guided Practice Use the glossary to find the meanings of the underlined words. Write the meanings on the lines.

HINT Use the first letter of the underlined word to help you find the word in the glossary.

1 Have you ever seen a <u>star</u> in the sky at night?

_____

2 It looks tiny from our <u>planet</u>, Earth.

_____

3 It really is a giant ball of hot <u>gas</u>.

_____

Independent Practice

Use the glossary to find the meaning of each underlined word.

> **close** near *My friend's house is close to mine.*
> **glowing** shining *At night she could see her cat's glowing eyes.*
> **heat** what makes things warm *I can feel the heat from the campfire.*
> **plant** something that is alive but is not an animal or person *A tree is a plant.*

1 What does the word "glowing" mean in this sentence?

The sun is a large, glowing star.

A burning **C** warm

B shining **D** pretty

2 What does the word "close" mean in this sentence?

It looks big because it is close to Earth.

A above **C** beside

B below **D** near

3 What does the word "plants" mean in this sentence?

The sun helps plants grow.

A boys and girls

B living things

C dog and cats

D things that crawl

4 What does the word "heat" mean in this sentence?

It also gives off heat that keeps us warm.

A what makes things cold

B something that puts out a fire

C what makes things warm

D something that scares people

Lesson 24
Real-Life Connections

L.2.5a: Identify real-life connections between words and their use (e.g., describe foods that are *spicy* or *juicy*).

Introduction When you read, you can connect words to your own life to make their meaning clearer.

You read:	You might think:
Some things taste salty.	Salty **popcorn makes me thirsty.**
Some things sound loud.	**My sister plays** loud **music.**

Guided Practice Circle the correct word or words to complete each sentence.

HINT Look at the answer choices. Ask yourself questions such as, "Have I ever eaten garlic? honey? ice? Which one tasted sweet?"

1 Something sweet might taste like _____.

garlic   ice   honey

2 Something quiet might sound like a _____.

fire alarm   whisper   thunderstorm

3 Something soft might feel like a _____.

kitten's fur   rock   bottle of water

4 Something round might look like a _____.

ball   flute   box

5 Something sweet might smell like a _____.

fish   flower   trash can

Independent Practice

Choose the correct answer to each question.

1 What is something you can <u>taste</u>?

   A a tall building

   B a juicy orange

   C a squeaky door

   D a sticky piece of tape

2 What is something you can <u>feel</u>?

   A a friend singing

   B a dinner cooking

   C a soft pillow

   D a TV show

3 What is something you can <u>smell</u>?

   A a honking horn

   B a cloud in the sky

   C a smooth sidewalk

   D a smoky fire

4 What is something you can <u>hear</u>?

   A a buzzing bee

   B a glass of milk

   C a piece of wood

   D a shining star

Lesson 25
Shades of Meaning

L.2.5b: Distinguish shades of meaning among closely related verbs (e.g., *toss, throw, hurl*) and closely related adjectives (e.g., *thin, slender, skinny, scrawny*).

Introduction Some words have almost the same meanings, but some meanings are stronger than others. **Strong words** tell exactly or most clearly what is happening in a sentence.

• Think about which word shown in green is the strongest.

> We get up when we hear the fire alarm.
>
> We stand up when we hear the fire alarm.
>
> We jump up when we hear the fire alarm.

• The word *jump* is the strongest. It tells most clearly what the students do when they hear the alarm.

Not Strong	Stronger	Strongest
get	stand	jump

Guided Practice Read each pair of sentences. Look at the underlined words. Circle the word with the strongest meaning.

HINT Picture in your mind what happens during a fire drill. Choose the word that tells most clearly what is happening.

1 Ms. Diaz <u>says</u>, "It's a fire drill. Line up at the door."
Ms. Diaz <u>shouts</u>, "It's a fire drill. Line up at the door."

2 We all feel a little <u>bad</u>.
We all feel a little <u>scared</u>.

3 We <u>go</u> out to the playground.
We <u>hurry</u> out to the playground.

4 Everyone on the <u>big</u> playground is quiet.
Everyone on the <u>huge</u> playground is quiet.

👤 Independent Practice

Circle the word in the box that best completes each sentence.

1 Read the sentence below.

The fire truck _____ up the street to the school.

Which word tells most clearly how fast the fire truck goes?

comes	races	moves	hurries

2 Read the sentence below.

_____ firefighters run into the school.

Which word tells exactly how many firefighters there are?

Some	Few	Several	Five

3 Read the sentence below.

Smiling, they _____ out the door of the school.

Which word tells most clearly how they leave the building?

come	march	move	walk

4 Read the sentence below.

This fire drill was _____!

Which word tells most clearly about how the fire drill went?

good	okay	excellent	fine

Lesson 26
Using Adjectives and Adverbs to Describe

L.2.6 Use words and phrases acquired through conversations, reading and being read to, and responding to texts, including using adjectives and adverbs to describe (e.g., *When other kids are happy that makes me happy*).

Introduction When you write, choose **adjectives** and **adverbs** that make your ideas clear and interesting.

- Use the best adjective you know to tell about a noun. An **adjective** can tell how something looks, smells, tastes, sounds, or feels.

> Sue heard a squeaky noise.
>
> She smelled sweet muffins baking.
>
> Bright light came through the window.

- Use the best adverb you know to tell about a verb. An **adverb** can tell about how, where, or when something happens.

> Sue woke up late.
>
> She dressed quickly.
>
> She ran downstairs.

Guided Practice Choose the adjective or adverb in parentheses ( ) that best completes each sentence. Write the word on the line.

HINT Try each answer choice in the sentence. Does the sentence make sense?

1 Sue hears a _____ horn.
(loud   happy)

2 The bus came _____!
(tomorrow   early)

3 Sue grabs her _____ backpack.
(warm   heavy)

4 Dad says, "We have to run _____!"
(quickly   slowly)

Independent Practice

Choose the correct word to complete each sentence.

1 The _____ school bus stops.

  A hungry

  B yellow

  C round

  D sleepy

2 Sue climbs _____ .

  A inside

  B after

  C down

  D outside

3 She finds an _____ seat.

  A excited

  B angry

  C unhappy

  D empty

4 She smiles and waves _____ to her dad.

  A meanly

  B noisily

  C happily

  D badly